NORTH SEA OIL IN THE FUTURE

North Sea Oil in the Future

Economic Analysis and Government Policy

COLIN ROBINSON
and
JON MORGAN

for the
Trade Policy Research Centre
London

First published 1978 by
THE MACMILLAN PRESS LTD
London and Basingstoke
*Associated companies in Delhi Dublin Hong Kong
Johannesburg Lagos Melbourne New York Singapore Tokyo*

Printed in Great Britain by
Billing & Sons Limited, Guildford, London and Worcester

British Library Cataloguing in Publication Data

Robinson, Colin, b. 1932
North Sea oil in the future
1. Offshore oil industry — North Sea
2. Energy policy — Europe
I. Title   II. Morgan, Jon   III. Trade
Policy Research Centre
333.8′2   HD9575
ISBN 0–333–23772–2
ISBN 0–333–25391–4Pbk

Robinson and Morgan
NORTH SEA OIL IN THE FUTURE

ERRATA

The lower column sub-heading on the right-hand side of Tables 8.1 to 8.9
inclusive (pages 158-74) should read '(£'000 million sterling at current prices)'.

Trade Policy Research Centre

The Trade Policy Research Centre in London was established in 1968 to promote independent analysis and public discussion of commercial and other international economic policy issues. It is a privately sponsored non-profit organisation and is essentially an entrepreneurial centre under the auspices of which a variety of activities are conducted. As such, the Centre provides a focal point for those in business, the universities and public affairs who are interested in international economic questions.

The Centre is managed by a Council which is headed by Sir Frank McFadzean. The members of the Council, set out below, represent a wide range of experience and expertise.

Having general terms of reference, the Centre does not represent any consensus of opinion. Intense international competition, technological advances in industry and agriculture and new and expanding markets, together with large-scale capital flows, are having profound and continuing effects on international production and trading patterns. With the increasing integration and interdependence of the world economy there is thus a growing necessity to increase public understanding of the problems now being posed and of the kind of solutions that will be required to overcome them.

The principal function of the Centre is the sponsorship of research programmes on policy problems of national and international importance. Specialists in universities and private firms are commissioned to carry out the research and the results are published and circulated in academic, business and government circles throughout the European Community and in other countries. Meetings and seminars are also organised from time to time.

Publications are presented as professionally competent studies worthy of public consideration. The interpretations and conclusions in them are those of their authors and do not purport to represent the views of the Council and others associated with the Centre.

The Centre is registered in the United Kingdom as an educational trust under the Charities Act 1960. It and its research programmes are financed by foundation grants, corporate donations and membership subscriptions.

Contents

List of Tables

List of Figures

Biographical Notes

COLIN ROBINSON has been Professor of Economics at the University of Surrey since 1968. He is a member of the Electricity Supply Research Council and is on the editorial boards of *Energy Policy* and *Applied Economics*. Before his present appointment, Professor Robinson was a business economist, mainly in the oil industry. He was head of the economics division, in the corporate planning department, of Esso Petroleum and was then economic adviser to Esso Europe's natural gas division during the first negotiations on North Sea gas contracts. Professor Robinson is the author of *Business Forecasting: an Economic Approach* (1971) and co-author, with George F. Ray, of *The European Energy Market in 1980* (1975) and, with Jon Morgan, of *North Sea Oil and the British Economy* (1977). In addition, he is the author of a number of papers on energy policy, including *A Policy for Fuel?* (1969), *Competition for Fuel* (1971), *The Energy Crisis and British Coal* (1974), and *Energy Depletion and the Economics of OPEC* (1975), besides numerous articles in professional publications.

JON MORGAN, now an economist with the British National Oil Corporation, was from 1974 to 1977 a Research Fellow in the Department of Economics at the University of Surrey, having completed his doctorate at Stirling University, where his thesis was on the technological economics of mineral resource development. He was earlier a geologist with Robertson Research International after graduating from the University of Oxford in 1970. Dr Morgan is the author, with Colin Robinson, of *North Sea Oil and the British Economy* (1977) and a number of articles, as listed in the Preface.

Preface

The research on which this book for the Trade Policy Research Centre is based goes back to the beginning of 1975 when the two authors started an investigation, in the Department of Economics at the University of Surrey, of the supply side of North Sea oil, assisted by a research fellowship for Jon Morgan provided by the Social Science Research Council. At that time there was hardly any information on North Sea costs, the tax system had not been devised and no oil had been produced: consequently we had to begin with a blank sheet of paper, collect our own statistical data and construct our own computer programs. When the SSRC funds ran out at the end of 1976, we were fortunate in being able to continue the work, and to complete this book, with the aid of a research fellowship kindly donated by the British National Oil Corporation. We are particularly grateful to Lord Kearton and to Alastair Morton, the Chairman and Managing Director respectively of BNOC, for their help. Research on North Sea oil is now continuing at the University of Surrey assisted by a research fellowship from Shell UK Limited.

Many people have contributed to the work which is described in this book, although the authors are, of course, responsible for the details of the work and, too, for the views expressed. A particular debt is owed to a number of people in the oil industry who gave their time to reading our working papers and to talking to us about the finer details of the economics and the technology of exploiting North Sea oil. We gratefully acknowledge help from numerous individuals in most of the major oil companies and would especially mention the valuable discussions we have had with John Sayers. We have also had the benefit of many helpful conversations and seminar discussions with our colleagues in the Department of Economics at the University of Surrey (where there is a thriving research activity in energy economics) who provided the environment in which this kind of book can be written. Computing assistance and advice were given to us by Ken Knight of the University's Department of Physics, whose computing facilities were used extensively.

In sponsoring the volume, the Trade Policy Research Centre's interest in North Sea oil questions has been assisted institutionally by a grant from the Ford Foundation, in New York, which has enabled the Centre to embark on a number of 'new' fields of enquiry.

Several chapters in the book are based on material previously published and we are grateful to the institutes and publishers concerned for giving us permission to make use of such material. The following papers by us both were drawn upon: *Economic Consequences of Controlling the Depletion of North Sea Oil and Gas*, Guest Paper No. 3 (London: Trade Policy Research Centre, 1976); 'World Oil Prices and the Profitability of North Sea Oil', *Petroleum Review*, London, April 1976; 'Depletion Control and Profitability: the Case of the North Sea', *Energy Policy*, Guildford, September 1976; *Effects of North Sea Oil on the United Kingdom's Balance of Payments*, Guest Paper No. 5 (London: Trade Policy Research Centre, 1976); 'Comparative Effects of the UK and Norwegian Oil Tax Systems on Profitability and Government Revenue', *Accounting and Business Research*, Exeter, Winter 1976; and *North Sea Oil and the British Economy* (London: Staniland Hall, 1977). We also drew on the article by Colin Robinson, 'The Energy Market and Energy Planning', *Long Range Planning*, London, December 1976.

The manuscript of the book was typed with great speed and efficiency by Mrs Averil Heaton in the Department of Economics at the University of Surrey; and we thank her also for a number of suggestions which made the final version of this book an improvement on our earlier drafts.

COLIN ROBINSON
JON MORGAN

Guildford
November 1977

Abbreviations

API	American Petroleum Institute
BNOC	British National Oil Corporation
BODL	Burmah Oil Development Limited
BP	British Petroleum
Btu	British thermal unit
cfd	cubic feet per day
c.i.f.	cost insurance and freight
CPI	crude price indexation
DCF	discounted cash flow
f.o.b.	free on board
GDP	Gross Domestic Product
GNP	Gross National Product
IRR	internal rates of return
LPD	limited price decline
m.t.c.e.	million tonnes coal equivalent
nNS	no North Sea
NPV	net present value
NS	North Sea
OECD	Organisation for Economic Cooperation and Development
OPEC	Organisation of Petroleum Exporting Countries
PRT	Petroleum Revenue Tax
ST	Special Tax
UKOOA	United Kingdom Offshore Operators' Association
UMP	use of monopoly power

CHAPTER 1

North Sea Oil and the World Economy

INTERNATIONAL OIL MARKET IN TRANSITION

The discovery of oil in the North Sea came at a critical time in the history of the world oil market. From the genesis of the modern oil industry – generally dated at the sinking of 'Colonel' Drake's well in Pennsylvania in 1859 – the industry had expanded rapidly. Wartime periods apart, world oil production had risen steadily year after year as technological changes allowed oil to take an increasing share of the energy market: from a lubricant and a fuel for lamps, it became the power-source for the increasing numbers of motor vehicles and aeroplanes, substituted for coal in electricity generating plants and in general industrial use and, by the 1960s, provided the feedstock for the fast-growing petrochemical industry. Figure 1.1 (logarithmic vertical scale) shows the growth of world oil output from 1860 to 1970. After very large percentage rates of increase in the early years the average annual compound rate of increase was near to 7 per cent from 1900 to 1970, implying an output doubling time of approximately ten years.[1]

During the rapid economic expansion of the 1960s and early 1970s the sharp upward trend in oil production and consumption continued and the absolute annual increases were, of course, very large compared with earlier experience. Between 1960 and 1973 the annual average compound rate of growth of world oil production was about 8 per cent, so that output in 1973 was over two and a half times its 1960 level (Table 1.1). In 1973 the *increase* over the previous year's output was approximately 230 million tonnes, which is about the same as the *total* annual world oil output in 1935. The 1960–73 period was also marked, as Table 1.1 shows, by the growing importance of the Middle East as a source of oil: nearly 45 per cent of the increase in world oil production came from that area.

In the energy markets of the industrial world, especially in Western Europe and Japan, oil substantially increased its market share during the 1960s principally because its price, relative to that of coal, its main

1

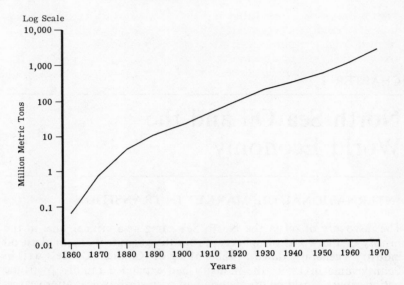

FIG. 1.1 World Oil Output (excluding Natural Gas Liquids), 1860–1970 at ten-year intervals

SOURCES British Petroleum, *Our Industry* (London, 1970); *BP Statistical Review of the World Oil Industry* (London, annual).

TABLE 1.1 World Oil Production, 1960–73

| | *million tonnes* | | |
	1960	*1973*	*Increase 1960–73*
North America	410.5	621.3	210.8
Middle East	261.8	1047.1	785.3
Latin America[a]	194.9	272.1	77.2
Africa	13.8	290.6	276.8
USSR, Eastern Europe and China	167.2	480.2	313.0
Others	42.4	132.8	90.4
Total	1090.6	2844.1	1753.5

[a] Including Mexico.

SOURCE *British Petroleum, Statistical Review of the World Oil Industry* (London, annual).

competitor, was falling.[2] The share of oil in world energy consumption rose from 32 per cent in 1960 to 45 per cent in 1973 (using United

Nations statistics – see Table 1.2) at the expense of coal, and most industrial countries became dependent on imported oil for a large part of their energy requirements. According to United Nations statistics[3] the share of oil (mostly imported) in Western Europe's energy consumption was almost 60 per cent in 1973 and it was over 75 per cent in Japan.

TABLE 1.2 World Consumption of Commercial Energy, 1960–73

	1960		1973	
	m.t.c.e.	% of total	m.t.c.e.	% of total
Solid fuels	2206	52	2503	32
Liquid fuels	1358	32	3598	45
Natural gas	594	14	1623	21
Hydro and nuclear electricity	85	2	186	2
Total	4243	100	7910	100

m.t.c.e. = million tonnes coal equivalent

SOURCE *World Energy Supplies, 1950–1974* (New York: United Nations, 1976).

With the benefit of hindsight, however, we can now see the 1960s and early 1970s as a rather unusual period in which, spurred on by rapid economic growth, the world oil industry experienced remarkable expansion accompanied, for much of the time, by falling relative prices. It is an interesting demonstration of how wrong the conventional wisdom about oil output and oil prices can be that so many believed during the 1960s that the real price of crude oil could continue to fall, into the indefinite future. Such views have been rudely shattered since the autumn of 1973 by extremely sharp crude-oil price increases and world recession which have combined to produce a change in trend in a major industry of a magnitude seldom observed. As Table 1.3 shows, after the rapid increases of the 1960–73 period, world oil production in 1974 was about the same as in 1973, in 1975 it fell about 5 per cent and in 1976, although output recovered and was greater than in 1973, much of the rise was due to end-year stockpiling in anticipation of the price increases by the Organisation of Petroleum Exporting Countries (OPEC) in December 1976. The change in trend is even more marked if one removes from the statistics production in the Soviet Union, Eastern Europe and China, which has continued to grow since 1973. Excluding these three areas,[4] it can be seen from Table 1.3 that oil output in the rest of the world fell more sharply in 1975 and in 1976 had still not regained its 1973 level. Comparing 1976 world oil output with prior expectations,

TABLE 1.3 World Oil Production, 1973–76

	World	million tonnes World, excluding USSR, E. Europe and China
1973	2850.8	2347.8
1974	2875.5	2329.8
1975	2732.4	2141.4
1976	2942.6	2312.0

Note The *Petroleum Economist* production statistics, which are the most up-to-date published source available, differ slightly from the BP figures used in Table 1.1. The trends shown by the estimates from the two sources are, however, very similar over the 1973–75 period.

SOURCE *The Petroleum Economist*, London, January 1976 and March 1977.

one can now see that it was several hundred million tonnes less than the projections which were made in the late 1960s and early 1970s.

THE ECONOMICS OF OPEC

It was in 1973 that large crude-oil price increases and Middle East output restrictions brought about the so-called oil crisis which forced the change in trend on to the public's attention. But there is a good case for arguing that the turning-point in the world oil industry came around 1970 — coincidentally, at just about the time the first North Sea oil discoveries were made. If we are to appreciate the significance of North Sea oil, we need to examine more closely the events of the last seven years and attempt to apply to them some simple economic analysis.[5]

It was in 1970 that limits on production imposed by the government of Libya first demonstrated the bargaining strength of the oil-exporting countries which, through their membership of the Organisation of Petroleum Exporting Countries, controlled over 90 per cent of world crude-oil exports. Table 1.4 shows the shares of individual OPEC member countries in world oil exports in 1972 — the year before the 'crisis'.

From 1970 onwards, fundamental changes in the world oil market began to take place. Prices rose steadily from 1970 to the autumn of 1973, when there began the price explosion which left world oil prices in mid-1977 probably about eight times what they had been in 1970 (Table 1.5). At the same time, the OPEC countries, by means of 'participation' agreements and nationalisation, took control of producing operations away from the oil companies.

'Explanations' of the actions of the oil producers abound, many of

TABLE 1.4 OPEC Exports of Crude Oil, 1972

OPEC Members	Million metric tonnes	Per cent of world total
Saudi Arabia	267.3	21.8
Iran	177.7	14.5
Kuwait	147.4	12.0
Iraq	67.2	5.5
Abu Dhabi	50.7	4.1
Qatar	21.5	1.8
Libya	106.4	8.7
Algeria	50.1	4.1
Nigeria	86.4	7.1
Venezuela	104.6	8.5
Indonesia	40.7	3.3
Total OPEC	1,120.0	91.4
Total World	1,224.6	100.0

SOURCES *Petroleum Times*, London, July 1973; Institute of Petroleum Information Service, London; *BP Statistical Review of the World Oil Industry* (London, 1972).

TABLE 1.5 Crude Oil Prices, 1965–77

| | Light Arabian[a] crude oil ($ per barrel) | |
	'Posted' price	State sales price
1965	1.80	—
end October 1970	1.80	—
end October 1973	5.12	—
January 1974	11.65	—
November 1974	11.25	10.46
Oct 1975	12.38	11.51
January 1977	—	12.09
July 1977	—	12.70

[a] Light Arabian crude oil, with an API gravity of 34°, quoted f.o.b. Persian Gulf in $US per barrel, has for some years been the accepted 'marker' crude oil. Other crude prices, however, do not always keep in step with Light Arabian, as was demonstrated at the December 1976 meeting of OPEC, when varying price increases were applied to different crudes (see *The Petroleum Economist*, London, February 1977, pp. 42–3). It is not easy to give precise figures of representative oil prices during the 1970s because of the move away from the old 'posted' (tax reference) price system. Market prices are now effectively set by the state sales prices established by the OPEC countries: up to 1970 they tended to be below posted prices. The increase in the market price of Saudi Arabian light crude from 1970 to early 1977 seems to have been from about $1.50 to $12 per barrel.

them concentrating on such proximate causes as the October War of 1973. But there are some fundamental economic features of the oil market in the early 1970s which need examination since, whatever political factors may have been at work, price increases of the magnitude of those in 1973–75 can hardly occur unless economic circumstances are propitious.

The first and most obvious feature of the oil market which helps to explain the behaviour of the oil producers in the 1970s is the tendency towards cartelisation. The market demand for crude oil is inelastic with respect to price, at least in the short and medium terms. For example, substantial economies in the use of oil in response to a price increase relative to other fuels take time, since one must either increase the efficiency with which oil is used or substitute other fuels: in either case, minor savings apart, investment is required and significant reductions in oil use may take some years to achieve. Calculations made from an econometric model for the countries of the European Community[6] suggest that the price elasticity of demand for oil is of the order of 0.15 in the short term: that is, a 1 per cent increase in the price of oil relative to other fuels may result in a reduction in oil consumption of only about one-seventh of 1 per cent in the first year or so. Over a longer period, however, the calculated price elasticity increases to about 0.6. In the technical economic sense, even the longer-run estimate is 'inelastic' (less than one) so that increases in the market price are likely to yield the oil producers an increase in revenues since the percentage reduction in volumes sold should be less than the percentage increase in price.

By contrast to the inelasticity of *total* market demand with respect to price, the price elasticity *for individual crude oils* is high. Crude oils vary in characteristics such as gravity, sulphur content and distance from market, but nevertheless they are good substitutes one for another and even small price differences among producers can significantly affect sales.

In markets where total demand is price-inelastic but the individual products within the market are price-elastic, producers have an incentive to band together to suppress competition within the group and to exploit the inelasticity of market demand. Such action is relatively straightforward in crude oil where, as Table 1.4 shows, a small number of countries controls a very large proportion of world trade. One might reasonably argue that OPEC is the strongest 'cartel' which the world has so far seen, even though it has no explicit output-sharing arrangement of the sort traditionally associated with a cartel.

Although susceptibility to cartelisation was a necessary condition for the events of the early 1970s, it was by no means sufficient. The elasticity characteristics of the oil market, discussed above, have been true for many years without promoting huge price increases. Indeed, if there was any kind of cartel in operation in the 1960s it was extraordinarily ineffective. Market prices of oil were falling in many industrialised countries as supplies of crude oil increased and as competition strengthened, so there was clearly no oil *company* cartel in operation. Nor did the producing *countries* manage to regulate the supply side of the market. OPEC was formed in 1960 and yet its members improved their real revenues per barrel very little in the subsequent ten years – as Table 1.6 shows. Total revenues of the oil-producing countries rose considerably because of the expansion of oil output, but there was no evidence of output-restricting price-increasing behaviour such as one might expect from a cartel.

TABLE 1.6 Producing Government Revenues per Barrel:
Light Arabian Crude Oil

	$	$1950[a]
1950	0.28	0.28
1960	0.68	0.55
1965	0.81	0.63
1970	0.89	0.61

[a] Government revenue per barrel divided by United Nations index of unit value of world exports of manufactured goods with time base adjusted to 1950 = 100.

SOURCE Colin Robinson, *Energy Depletion and the Economics of OPEC* (London: Henley Centre for Forecasting, 1975) p. 15.

The transition from the 1960s – with rising output and declining market prices in real terms – to the early 1970s, when OPEC became steadily more assertive, is an economic phenomenon of unusual interest. A number of possible explanations can be suggested. First, and most obvious, one would not have expected OPEC to be very aggressive in its early years. The original founders – Iran, Iraq, Kuwait, Saudi Arabia and Venezuela – had as their first objective to stop any further *reductions* in posted prices of crude oil, like those made in 1959 and 1960 by the oil companies. At that time the producers lacked confidence in their ability to hold together and to exploit the market. No doubt such confidence grew as time went by, as they held together and as the attitude of the developing countries towards the industrialised world began to change. One element in the assertiveness of OPEC in the 1970s was the view of some of its members that they were leading a challenge to the industrial countries by the developing world and compensating for past 'exploitation'. They were quite prepared to use methods which in the past would have been considered violent to attain their ends. The Arab members of OPEC were also, of course, concerned to change the attitude of the West towards Middle East problems. One must look, however, beyond such political explanations of oil-producer behaviour at some of the economic features of the situation.

Consider the following simple model of oil-producer behaviour, which is based on the economist's theory of non-renewable resource depletion. Assume that a producer (government or company) with given reserves has as his objective the maximisation of the expected net present value of those reserves. That is to say, he has a number of possible production profiles through time, within certain technical limits, and he selects the one which gives him maximum revenue when discounted back to the present. In these circumstances it can be shown that the maximisation conditions amount to the producer's so adjusting his output programme that his expected per barrel 'take' in each production period has the same discounted value. Or what amounts to the same thing, his expected take per barrel will, under the optimum production programme, increase at a rate equal to his discount rate.

To fix the point, rather than going into the mathematics take an arithmetic example. Our hypothetical producer has a choice between:

(*a*) leaving a barrel of oil under the desert where it can give him no return other than an appreciation in its price net of costs and taxes (p); and,

(*b*) producing the barrel and investing the proceeds at whatever interest rate he expects to obtain (i).

Let us say that the present net price (p) is \$11, that the expected interest rate (i) is 12 per cent and that the expected appreciation in the net price over time (t)

$$\left(\frac{\mathrm{d}p}{\mathrm{d}t} = \dot{p} \right)$$

is 15 per cent. Then the producer who wants to maximise the net present value of his reserves will keep his barrel in the ground. If he produces it and invests his \$11, it will have grown to \$19.4 in five years' time; whereas the net price of a barrel left in the ground would, on our assumptions, increase at 15 per cent per annum to over \$22 in five years.

Though the example is simplified it demonstrates that the net present value maximising oil producer is interested in two things: prospective net price appreciation ($\dot{p}$) which is the return on oil kept in the ground, and the return he can expect to earn on other investments (i). If $\dot{p} > i$, as in our example, oil will tend to be held in the ground so that planned output programmes will tend to be reduced. If $\dot{p} < i$ output will tend to be increased.

Theories based on expectations are difficult to test but the model appears to give a good explanation of producer behaviour both in the 1960s and at the turning-point in the early 1970s. Two important features of the 1960s stand out. First, expectations of declining prices were generated — in other words p was negative, so that with a positive i one would expect a tendency to extract oil in the present rather than holding it back until the presumed lower-priced future. The reasons why declining prices were expected are complex but they probably originated at the time when United States import restrictions pushed oil, newly discovered by United States 'independents', onto European and Japanese markets and they were strengthened by the second feature of the 1960s to which we now turn.

It seems very likely that in the 1960s not only was p negative but i was unusually high. The oil companies, who still controlled depletion rates in the OPEC countries at this time, were well aware that it was only a question of time before the producing governments took control of oil operations in their territories: in other words their time-horizons were shortened, their discount rates were consequently abnormally high and they had an incentive to produce 'now' not only because prices might be lower in the future but because per barrel profits on future state-owned oil might well be lower.

How then did the market change? In addition to the political factors already mentioned there were significant changes both in p and i which reversed their relationship. As producing governments took control of production decisions (not necessarily by nationalisation but effectively, nevertheless) discount rates declined. This is not to suggest that governments generally have longer time-horizons than private companies — only that the horizons of these particular governments were longer in the second half of the 1960s than the horizons of oil companies, which were abnormally short because of feared political action. At the same time that i was declining, p was clearly increased. By the early 1970s there was a chorus of 'doomsters' predicting shortages of raw materials and especially oil. In effect, this was a message to the oil producers that they were sitting on a very valuable material which would appreciate rapidly in the future. The message was quickly received. It was natural for the oil producers, smarting under what they believed to be 'exploitation' in the past to say: 'if in the 1980s, why not now?' Price appreciation prospects looked good and it seemed they could be improved by holding back output. $p > i$, so output was restricted, prices soared and the events of the early 1970s were set in train. For a while it seemed that the oil producers, by restricting production, could create price rises and expectations of further increases which would make them want to cut output still more.

The price appreciation/interest rate model seems to be a useful taxonomic device within which to analyse various features of a complex market and it does appear to provide an explanation of some apparently puzzling features of the 1960s and 1970s. It is not strictly necessary to assume that oil producers are net present value *maximisers* for the p/i model to work: all that we need to assume is that there is some preference for a greater (not necessarily a maximum) net present value rather than a smaller. In considering depletion policy in Chapter 2 a similar model is used.

IMPACT OF THE NORTH SEA ON THE WORLD OIL MARKET

Summarising, it can be said that the discovery of oil in the northern North Sea has coincided with a turning-point in the world energy market. After rising substantially in the 1960s, world oil output is no longer increasing; oil prices, which tended to fall in real terms in the 1960s, have in the last few years been forced upwards – at a rate probably unprecedented for such an important commodity – by the action of a group of producers with a near-monopoly of world exports; and, because the price is monopoly-determined yet the constituents of OPEC have a great diversity of interests, there is considerable uncertainty about future movements in oil prices. If the price of oil had been rising as a consequence of increasing scarcity, prediction would have been somewhat easier. As it is, no one knows to what extent the world oil price diverges from what it would have been in competitive conditions and it is very difficult to foresee the behaviour of the individual members of OPEC and their influence on future prices.

The impact on the North Sea of world oil market conditions, the effect of price on North Sea profitability and the problem of making decisions about North Sea development in the face of uncertainties originating in the world market, will all be recurring themes in this book. The rest of this chapter provides a general introduction to North Sea development and its relationship to the international oil industry.

Since 1964 development of the North Sea has proceeded at remarkable speed and the area is now established as a major oil and gas province. In the early days attention was concentrated on the relatively shallow waters of the southern part of the British North Sea with natural gas as the principal target. Success came rapidly. The necessary British legislation (the Continental Shelf Act) was passed in 1964, by October 1965 British Petroleum had made the first gas strike in the West Sole field, and a series of larger discoveries in 1966 and 1967 showed that the British sector of the southern North Sea is a significant gas-bearing region with recoverable reserves of the order of 25 to 30 million cubic feet – sufficient to support output of some 4000 million cubic feet per day (41,000 million cubic metres per year) for a nominal twenty-year depletion period. Subsequently there were gas finds in the Northern Basin (some of associated gas, such as the Brent field) and at least one major gas discovery (Frigg) was made on the British/Norwegian median line.

One effect of these successes in gas exploration was to transform the previously slow-growing British gas industry as Chapter 2 (pages 21–22) shows. By late 1976 virtually the whole of the British gas distribution network had been converted from manufactured gas to carry natural gas of about twice the calorific value.

Important as were the natural gas discoveries, North Sea oil finds were to be even more significant. By the end of the 1960s, the main focus of interest in the North Sea had switched to the northern area, where water depths are much greater than in the south. The oil companies felt that the large gas-bearing structures in the south had already been located and they were also disappointed by the price paid in the first natural gas contracts by the Gas Council (now the British Gas Corporation), which the government had decided should be virtually the sole buyer of natural gas. Consequently the companies had an incentive to improve deep-water exploration and production technology and to move into the northern areas where the prospects seemed better for oil (which did not have to be sold to the Gas Council) than for gas. At the same time, exploration was proceeding in the Norwegian sector of the North Sea and the first big North Sea oil strike was in fact made in Norwegian waters when the large Ekofisk field was discovered by the Phillips group in November 1969. During the next six years there were numerous oil discoveries, mainly in the British sector, though another large field (Statfjord) was found on the Norwegian side of the median line.

The first substantial quantities of North Sea oil began to flow in mid-1975; deliveries by tanker from the relatively small Argyll field started in summer 1975, followed by pipeline deliveries to Britain from the Norwegian Ekofisk field and from British Petroleum's Forties field in the British sector. Production of North Sea oil increased rapidly in 1976 and 1977 (Table 1.7). The precise timing of the production build-up over the next few years is necessarily somewhat uncertain, because there may well be accidents and unforeseen delays of various sorts, but the chances are that by about 1980 output of British sector North Sea oil will be around 100 million tonnes.[7] To put this into the perspective of the United Kingdom energy market as a whole, Table 1.8 gives some estimates of total consumption of energy and its constituents in 1980. The table suggests that, by that time, North Sea oil supplies of 100 million tonnes would be equivalent to 40 to 50 per cent of United Kingdom energy consumption (though not all North Sea oil will actually be sold in the United Kingdom). With North Sea gas supplies of about 6000 million cubic feet per day (roughly 62,000 million cubic metres per year), North Sea supplies as a fraction of the total British energy market could rise from less than one-fifth in 1975 to over two-thirds in 1980, bringing about virtual energy self-sufficiency in the arithmetic sense that supplies of indigenously-produced oil, gas, coal,

TABLE 1.7 Production of Oil from the British Sector of the North Sea[a]

Year	Quarter	Million tonnes
1975	III	0.3
	IV	1.0
1976	I	1.3
	II	2.4
	III	3.1
	IV	5.3
1977	I	7.7
	II	9.7
	III	10.1
	IV	10.4

[a] Including natural gas liquids and a small quantity of onshore production.

SOURCE *Energy Trends*, Department of Energy, London, various issues.

TABLE 1.8 United Kingdom Inland Primary Energy Consumption

	Million tonnes coal or coal equivalent	
	1975	*1980 Forecast*
Coal	120	110 ± 10
Oil[a]	136	140 ± 10
Natural Gas	56	80 ± 5
Nuclear	11	23 ± 3
Hydro	2	2
	325	355 ± 10
Output as percent of energy consumption:		
North Sea gas	17	23 ± 1
North Sea oil	1	48 ± 5
	18	71 ± 6

[a] Excluding non-energy products.

SOURCE OF 1975 STATISTICS *Digest of United Kingdom Energy Statistics* 1976 (London: Department of Energy, 1976).

hydro and nuclear electricity would be about equal to United Kingdom energy consumption.

North Sea oil and gas are even more significant in the Norwegian energy market, which is less than one-tenth the size of the British market. Norway, despite its 'go-slow' exploitation policy (see Chapter 2, pages 26–9) appears destined to become a substantial net oil exporter. By 1980 it seems likely that production of oil and gas from the Norwegian sector of the North Sea will be around 55 million tonnes oil equivalent, whereas Norwegian oil and gas consumption will be the equivalent of no more than 10 million tonnes of oil.[8]

There are two ways in which one might attempt to put North Sea oil supplies into the context of the world oil market. One is to compare North Sea reserves with world reserves and the other is to compare annual rates of output over the next few years.

In Chapter 3, estimates are given of recoverable reserves (that is, oil in place multiplied by the proportion likely to be recovered) in the British sector of the North Sea south of 62° North. Such estimates are sensitive to future variations in costs, prices and taxes and to changes in recovery technology, but it may be that reserves eventually recovered from this area will be in the range 20,000 to 30,000 million barrels (approximately 3000 to 4000 million tonnes). Taking into account the Norwegian sector, which has been less intensively explored than the British, the area north of the 62nd Parallel and the seas to the west and south of Britain, it is conceivable that eventual recovery will be as much as twice these figures. An estimate by J. D. Moody, of Mobil Oil,[9] suggested that ultimate crude-oil recovery from the North Sea might be about 50,000 million barrels (nearly 7000 million tonnes), although Moody attached wide error bands to his figures as indeed one must given that knowledge of the North Sea is so limited at present.

It may well be another five to ten years before production experience has accumulated and sufficient exploration has been carried out to make reasonably confident predictions of the North Sea's potential. However, to set North Sea reserves in the context of the world total one can make some rough comparisons. For example, Moody's estimate of eventual recovery of crude oil from the world as a whole is 2 million million barrels (about 270,000 million tonnes) so that, on his figures, North Sea recoverable reserves are some $2\frac{1}{2}$ per cent of the world total. Similarly, recoverable reserves already proved in the North Sea seem to be of the order of 2 to 3 per cent of world proved oil reserves. Such figures should not be interpreted too precisely. Apart from the problems of assessing reserves in a new production area such as the North Sea, world oil resources may in the end turn out to be a good deal larger than people imagine at present. There has for some years been an expert consensus that eventual world crude-oil recovery will be approximately 2 million million barrels but no one can be sure how changes in economic conditions and technology will affect oil recovery in the future: if oil from areas now considered commercially attractive becomes increasingly scarce it may well be that recovery rates will rise and oil will be

produced from regions which seem unattractive now and from uncon-
ventional sources.[10]

Despite all the reservations one should have about estimates of oil
reserves, the simple general point which can be made is that North Sea
oil reserves, large as they may appear to Britain and to Norway, are
relatively small in a world context – perhaps one should be no more
precise than to suggest that they are likely to be between 1 and 4 per cent
of the world total, with a central estimate of around $2\frac{1}{2}$ per cent.

Given the comparatively small size of North Sea reserves the
producers of oil in the North Sea, although they are typically
subsidiaries of large oil companies or big United Kingdom corporations
(private and public), are unlikely to have any substantial market power
qua North Sea producers. As far as they are concerned, the price at
which they sell their product is exogenously determined by the members
of OPEC: each North Sea producer must feel that he is a price-taker
facing a more or less horizontal demand curve for his output, so that he
can sell as much as he can produce without significantly influencing
price.

In the long term it seems improbable that the availability of North Sea
oil will have any great effect on world oil prices, unless North Sea
supplies turn out to be far greater than is expected at present. The world
long-run oil-supply curve will be shifted to the right, so that prices will
presumably be rather lower than they would otherwise have been, but
the effect seems unlikely to be large. Nevertheless, in the next few years,
North Sea oil might have a much more significant influence on the world
oil market in which, as we have seen, the present price level is monopoly-
determined.

To appreciate the effect, attention must be concentrated on the build-
up of North Sea production from now to the mid-1980s, rather than on
reserves. During this period, output of North Sea oil is likely to increase
very fast, displacing exports which would otherwise have been made by
OPEC; some further substitution for OPEC oil may come from the rise
in North Sea natural-gas output. Although there is considerable
uncertainty about North Sea output in the mid-1980s (see Chapter 3), a
reasonable guess is that it will be in the region of 200 million tonnes of oil
and 70 to 80 million tonnes oil equivalent of natural gas. This would
represent an *increase* in North Sea output, as compared with 1976, of
(say) 200 to 220 million tonnes oil equivalent (Table 1.9). Such figures
are quite considerable in relation to OPEC output of about 1500 million
tonnes in 1976: they are sufficient to avoid an increase of 13 to 15 per
cent (1.4 to 1.6 per cent per annum from a 1976 base to 1985) in demand
for OPEC oil which would presumably have occurred had there been no
North Sea oil. Such an outward shift in the demand curve for OPEC oil
would clearly have put upward pressure on world oil prices, so the North
Sea can be seen as a fairly powerful price-restraining or price-decreasing

TABLE 1.9 Output of Oil and Gas from the North Sea, 1976—85

| | | *Million tonnes oil equivalent* | | |
| | | | | *Increase* |
		1976	*1985 estimated*	*1976—85*
Oil	British sector	12	150	+ 138
	Norwegian sector	14	45	+ 31
Natural	British sector	33	52	+ 19
gas	Norwegian sector	3	27	+ 24
		62	274	+ 212

SOURCES *Energy Trends*, Department of Energy, London, various issues; *The Petroleum Economist*, London, January 1977, pp. 23—5; *World Energy Outlook* (Paris: Organisation for Economic Cooperation and Development, 1977) pp. 45—9.

influence during the period when its output is rising rapidly. How such influence will work out in practice can only be usefully discussed after looking at the total world demand and supply situation and, in particular, the effect of rising oil output from other non-OPEC sources such as Alaska, Mexico and China and of increasing United States oil imports. *If* there were to be only a slow growth in world oil consumption and *if* the expansion of non-OPEC supplies were to change the price expectations of OPEC members so that they no longer believed they could look forward to substantial price appreciation in the future, some OPEC countries might increase output and bring about some moderate price decline. But there are other possible scenarios which are presented in Chapter 6, where the sensitivity of North Sea supplies to world oil prices is examined.

Finally, in this broad introductory survey of the impact of the North Sea, it is worth mentioning its effect on the energy position of Western Europe generally and the European Community in particular. The discovery of large quantities of oil so close to the West European market is an unfamiliar blessing to an area accustomed to importing virtually all its oil and concerned to reduce its dependence on OPEC oil. Amid all the uncertainties and wrangling which surround the development of nuclear fission power it is helpful to have one indigenous energy source which can readily substitute for existing sources and the quantities of which seem reasonably assured.

Turning specifically to the European Community, one of its energy objectives appears to be to hold oil imports in the mid-1980s to about their 1973 (pre-'crisis') level. Obviously, such an aim would have been extraordinarily difficult without North Sea oil; it would probably have implied very large increases in the price of oil relative to other fuels.

Calculations of the oil prices necessary to keep Community oil imports in 1985 to their 1973 level have been made in the University of Surrey Economics Department[11] with the aid of an econometric model. The results suggest that, without North Sea oil, it might have been necessary to double market prices of oil relative to other fuels between 1975 and 1985 to restrain oil consumption sufficiently to achieve the constant oil imports objective. With North Sea oil, however, the required relative price increase could be as low as zero and seems unlikely to exceed 30 to 50 per cent.

This chapter has attempted to sketch in the background for the detailed economic analysis of North Sea oil which follows. North Sea oil, as we have seen, arrived at a time of fundamental change in the world oil market when a group of oil producers had taken advantage of the inelasticity of market demand to raise prices very sharply. Although North Sea oil reserves seem likely to represent only a few per cent of world reserves, the build-up of output over the next few years is likely to have significant effects on oil prices and the oil market in general. What this book attempts to do is to analyse the probable effects of government policy towards North Sea oil; how supplies may grow; the influence on profitability of costs, prices, the tax system and the rate of production; and the impact of North Sea oil on the British balance of payments and the wider economy.

NOTES AND REFERENCES

1. A useful source of statistics on the early history of the oil industry is: *Our Industry* (London: British Petroleum, 1970).
2. *Oil – The Present Situation and Future Prospects* (Paris: OECD,1973) ch. X.
3. Different sources of energy statistics give different market shares to individual fuels, mainly because of variations in the methods used to convert fuels to a common unit (such as coal equivalent, oil equivalent, therms) for aggregation purposes.
4. The resulting estimates are frequently known by the rather emotive term 'Free World' oil output.
5. More detailed comments are in: Colin Robinson, *Energy Depletion and the Economics of OPEC* (London: Henley Centre for Forecasting, 1975), and Robinson, 'The Energy Market and Energy Planning', *Long Range Planning*, London, December 1976.
6. Robinson and George Kouris, 'EEC Demand for Imported Crude Oil, 1956 to 1985', *Energy Policy*, Guildford, June 1977, gives details of the econometric model used in estimation, which was by a pooled cross-section/time-series method.
7. More details of estimated future production are given in Chapter 3.
8. George Ray and Robinson, *The European Energy Market in 1980* (London: Staniland Hall, 1975) vol. I.
9. J. D. Moody, 'An Estimate of the World's Recoverable Crude Oil Resource', *9th World Petroleum Congress*, Tokyo, May 1975.

10. For estimates of oil and other fossil-fuel resources and the difficulty of assessing resources, see Robinson, *The Energy 'Crisis' and British Coal* (London: Institute of Economic Affairs, 1974); and, Robinson, 'The Depletion of Energy Resources', in D. W. Pearce (ed.), *The Economics of Natural Resource Depletion* (London: Macmillan, 1975). A very good survey of world energy resources and the problems of estimating them is in D. C. Ion, *Availability of World Energy Resources* (London: Graham & Trotman, 1975).

11. Robinson and Kouris, *op. cit.*, gives estimates of the price changes necessary to hold imports constant and shows the sensitivity of the estimates to variations in the price and income elasticities. Estimated oil imports in 1985 on various price and income assumptions are also shown.

CHAPTER 2

Policy towards the Depletion of North Sea Oil

The importance of North Sea oil and gas to Britain, Norway and indeed to the rest of Western Europe, was discussed in Chapter 1.[1] Despite the significance of the North Sea, there is little sign that the rate at which reserves should be depleted has received more than cursory consideration, although the Norwegians have perhaps devoted more attention to depletion policy than the British. In general, ideas on depletion appear to have been dominated by vague notions that companies would, if left to themselves, produce offshore reserves too quickly, and that governments have major roles to play as regulators of output from the North Sea. Such ideas are in danger of being accepted into the popular wisdom without serious criticism, presumably because they fit in with two related, prevailing fashions – the British economic establishment's view that government intervention is almost invariably both benevolent and advantageous to society as a whole[2] and the 'conservationist' belief that private markets will not properly allocate resources as between present and future generations.

The objectives of this chapter are, first, to examine government policy towards the depletion of North Sea oil and gas over the last ten years, primarily in Britain but with a brief review of Norwegian policy also, in order to determine what has so far motivated governments. Second, it goes on to consider British legislation on the subject – principally the Petroleum and Submarine Pipelines Act of November 1975. Third, there is a short account of the economist's theory of resource depletion, followed by an examination of so-called market 'imperfections' which might be held to justify government intervention and of imperfections in the political process which mar the activities of 'real world' governments. The chapter also serves as a brief introduction to the history of North Sea exploitation since 1964.

PERIOD OF 'RAPID EXPLOITATION', 1964–74

During the first ten years of development of the United Kingdom's offshore area – that is, from the passing of the 1964 Continental Shelf Act until publication of the July 1974 White Paper on *United Kingdom Offshore Oil and Gas Policy*[3] – the policy of successive British governments was to exploit reserves of both natural gas and oil as rapidly as seemed possible. The Public Accounts Committee of the House of Commons, after considering evidence from the Department of Trade and Industry (previously the Ministry of Technology and the Ministry of Power) concluded early in 1973 that governments had decided

that the balance of advantage to the United Kingdom lay in exploiting and extracting these reserves of gas and oil as quickly as possible. In arriving at this decision they took into account relevant factors including balance of payments savings, security of supply, possible future fuel shortages, as well as the purely economic advantage judged, for both gas and oil, by comparisons of the estimated present net value of the resources if extracted earlier or later.[4]

The rapid exploitation policy was instituted in the mid-1960s when interest lay mainly in the potentially gas-bearing areas of the southern North Sea but, as Department of Trade and Industry representatives made clear to the Public Accounts Committee,[5] it was decided in 1968 that essentially the same policy should be applied as exploration effort concentrated on the search for oil in the northern North Sea. During this period companies were encouraged to explore and to develop finds quickly and the tax regime was undoubtedly attractive to private companies as compared with many other oil- and gas-producing areas.[6]

The precise meaning, in terms of depletion policy, of this apparently simple approach of 'exploiting and extracting . . . as quickly as possible' is not as straightforward as it might at first sight appear, because of the ambiguity in the phrase 'as quickly as possible'. There is, for example, some trade-off between the speed of exploitation and the eventual quantity of reserves recovered. Yet, as will be shown below, during the 1964–74 period governments seem generally to have been content to let depletion rates be producer-determined, although obviously the producers were expected to operate within the limits of 'good oilfield practice', to unitise (that is, operate as one unit any field which spreads over several blocks) where necessary and in other ways to work within the ground rules set by governments in the Petroleum (Production) Regulations (see below).

The legislation which governed offshore development reflected the policy of rapid exploitation in that there was no explicit mention of depletion control. The legislative basis was established by the 1964 Continental Shelf Act which, in effect, extended to the United Kingdom's offshore area the relevant provisions of the Petroleum (Production) Act of 1934 and under which were made various more detailed regulations known as the Petroleum (Production) Regulations of 1964, 1966 and 1971[7] which, *inter alia*, included 'model clauses' setting out the rights and obligations of the Minister and the licensee.

Although neither the Act nor the Regulations contains specific depletion control provisions, they do give very wide powers to the Minister, as has so often been the case in recent United Kingdom legislation. The model clauses in the Regulations are mainly concerned with technical details of licence termination, surrender, measuring and accounting for petroleum, working methods and obligations, unitisation and assignment rules and so on, although the Minister has power to vary particular provisions of the Regulations if he sees fit.[8] More important, though, are two sections of the Continental Shelf Act which could have been used to regulate depletion, had the Government wished to do so.

First is Section 6(1) which extends to the United Kingdom offshore area the duty laid on the Minister of Fuel and Power, in the 1945 Ministry of Fuel and Power Act, of securing the effective and coordinated development (of fuel and power). Since what is 'effective' and what is 'coordinated' must be purely matters of opinion, this clause seems to give the Minister *carte blanche* to regulate anything and everything to do with the fuel market, should he choose to do so. He could have maintained that depletion control was necessary for 'effective and coordinated development', though no doubt the producing companies would have argued that so general a provision in the law should not be used for so specific a purpose.

Second, it would have been possible to regulate the depletion rates of natural gas fields by using the effective monopsony rights to gas produced from the offshore area and used as fuel which Section 9 of the Act gives to the Gas Council and Boards (now the Gas Corporation). During the period under consideration only natural gas was being extracted from the North Sea: oil production began only in mid-1975 (see Chapter 1, Table 1.7). Since there was, in practice, a sole buyer of offshore natural gas and since that buyer was susceptible to ministerial pressure, either by directive or more likely by informal means, production rates could have been controlled by the Government through the Gas Council. Either the minimum quantities specified in the long-term contracts between the producers and the Council or the actual amounts taken by the Council could have been different from the producers' optimal depletion rates. There is, however, no evidence that such pressure was applied. Any ministerial intervention seems to have been to persuade the Gas Council that it should adjust as far as possible to the producers' preferred rates of output in order to build up natural gas supplies speedily.[9] The Government was clearly very concerned to achieve this rapid build-up. As the 1967 Fuel Policy White Paper says,

This policy [of rapid build-up in supplies] will mean a shorter life for the gas fields than a policy of slow depletion and will involve using some of the gas in markets where the resource savings are relatively low. The Government believe that these disadvantages are out-weighed by the value of giving an incentive to the further exploration needed to improve our knowledge of the ultimate resources available, and by the benefits to the economy and the balance of payments which a fast build-up of supplies will bring. [10]

The build-up rates for the three major natural gas fields involved in the 1966–68 negotiations between the companies and the Gas Council (Leman Bank, Indefatigable and Hewett) were perhaps rather slower than the producers would have wished because of the problems foreseen by the Council and Boards in the rapid expansion of gas distribution and marketing, but plateau rates of output [11] appear to have been roughly in accord with the producers' wishes. The Gas Council apparently acceded fairly readily to the Government's desire for rapid exploitation and planned for North Sea supplies to grow extremely fast. In 1965, the year before the major negotiations began, the British gas industry was supplying town gas equivalent to only just over 1000 million cubic feet per day (cfd) of natural gas [12] and the planned expansion was roughly a quadrupling of sales in ten years – that is, a compound growth rate of some 15 per cent per annum.

The big rise in natural gas sales which was actually achieved up to 1975 is shown in Table 2.1. The target of 4000 million cfd (about 14,500 million therms a year) was almost attained despite the recession in the economy, and by 1977 to all intents and purposes the gas distribution system in Britain had been converted to the direct use of natural gas.

In summary, government policy towards North Sea exploitation was, for ten years, characterised by a fairly successful effort to stimulate exploration activity, to achieve a rapid build-up of natural gas output and to induce plans to bring into operation quickly those North Sea oilfields which had been discovered. Producers appear to have been allowed to deplete gas fields and to plan to deplete oil fields without any significant government interference. Such official intervention as there was seems to have been directed principally at ensuring that the Gas Council did not place obstacles in the way of the rapid exploitation policy. In sharp contrast to their attitude towards pricing natural gas, governments seem generally to have been on the side of the producers as regards depletion rates. It was, of course, obvious to governments that to some extent rapid depletion could in the producers' eyes compensate for low prices by keeping up their discounted-cash-flow returns. It may well have been true that the reasons why the rapid exploitation policy was instituted were those given by the Government. It also seems to be true, however, that the rapid depletion policy became an indispensable complement to the 'low price' policy for natural gas. [13] Given that 'low

TABLE 2.1 Gas Available in Great Britain: Public Supply
(million therms)

Year	Natural gas[a]	Other	Total gas available
1950		2,616	2,616
1960	13	2,920	2,933
1965	271	3,481	3,752
1966	265	3,761	4,026
1967	480	3,859	4,339
1968	1,062	3,809	4,871
1969	1,973	3,513	5,486
1970	3,928	2,390	6,318
1971	6,682	1,365	8,047
1972	9,629	963	10,592
1973	10,596	1,018	11,614
1974	12,904	526	13,430
1975	13,588	211	13,799

[a] Mainly North Sea gas from 1968. Includes imports from Algeria of about 250 to 350 million therms a year from 1965. Natural gas supplied direct to consumers and natural gas re-formed to town gas are both included.

SOURCE *Digest of UK Energy Statistics* (London: H.M. Stationery Office, 1976).

price' was evidently regarded as a fixed point in the natural gas negotiations, it was necessary for some other variable to be adjusted if the producers were to retain an interest in the British offshore area, following their disappointment with the prices obtained in the 1966–68 contract negotiations.

A CHANGE OF MIND, 1974–75

The first official hint of reconsideration of the rapid exploitation policy became evident in January 1973 when witnesses from the then Department of Trade and Industry explained to the Public Accounts Committee of the House of Commons that, although rapid development was still the policy in operation, a review was in progress of 'the very vexed question of whether there would in certain circumstances be advantage in delaying the exploitation of our own resources of oil rather than expediting them'.[14] At that time a Conservative Government was in power, but by March 1974 a Labour Government was back in office on a manifesto which included some general references to the need for the development of the United Kingdom's offshore oil and gas to be under public control. Towards the end of May came the first clear indication of a change in attitude. According to a press report[15] Eric Varley, then Secretary of State for Energy, said that the Government was now taking a more conservationist attitude to oil and gas exploitation, 'substituting the idea of long-term balanced flow for the previous policy of as rapid development as possible'. Mr Varley was quoted as saying it would be 'utterly ludicrous to suggest we go for maximum production immediately': oil production should be looked at as a long-term prospect for the next forty or fifty years.

Other voices, too, were being raised against the rapid development policy. William Wolfe, chairman of the Scottish Nationalist Party, was reported as saying that his party's policy was to restrict offshore oil output to 50 million tons per annum.[16] Later in the year the Conservative Party proposed an independent body (to be called the Oil Conservation Authority) to regulate the rate of depletion of oil reserves, if need be, in the 1980s.[17]

Amid this apparent consensus that some form of explicit depletion control should be introduced, the Labour Government's White Paper on *United Kingdom Offshore Oil and Gas Policy* was published.[18] It had this to say on depletion control:

> The Government will, therefore, for current as well as future licences, take power to control the level of production in the national interest. This does not affect their determination to build up production as quickly as possible over the next few years. The question of reducing the rate of depletion is unlikely to arise for some years but the Government believe that they should take the necessary powers now.

In other words, the rapid development policy should continue for some years, but a reserve power should be introduced to reduce the rate of depletion should this become necessary. In broad outline this seems to be very similar to the policy later outlined by the Conservative Party and mentioned above. Although the mechanics of control would be different under the Conservatives, the major parties appeared to agree that there should be a rapid build-up to self-sufficiency in oil around 1980, by which time depletion control might become necessary. The Scottish Nationalists, on the other hand, apparently wanted immediate restrictions on output.

Before discussing the British Government's detailed proposals for depletion control, which were set out in the Petroleum and Submarine Pipelines Bill, published in April 1975 (and receiving Royal Assent in November), it is worth considering possible reasons why this consensus on the need for control developed in the two major political parties.

One obvious change which occurred during the latter part of the rapid exploitation period was that, as explained in Chapter 1, there appeared to be a radical alteration in the world energy market. From the early

1970s fears of shortages of energy and other non-renewable resources had been growing, stimulated by a number of works which, regardless of one's view of their inherent quality, were without doubt extremely influential.[19] This was in contrast to the prevailing view during the second half of the 1960s, when the United Kingdom's rapid exploitation policy was in operation and the first North Sea natural-gas contracts were being negotiated, at which time there was an expectation of further reductions in the price of energy, especially oil. In such circumstances, as explained in Chapter 1, producers of a depleting resource will tend to plan their output programmes in order to produce sooner rather than later.[20]

Similarly, a government which is considering whether depletion should be 'fast' or 'slow' is likely to go for the former. In assessing the present value of resource savings from natural gas and later oil, British governments used a discount rate of 10 per cent[21] and yet their most probable assumption about prices (net of costs) must have been for a rate of increase of much less than 10 per cent per annum. Although the precise results of calculations of resource savings will depend on what resources are assumed to be displaced by offshore oil and gas and when such displacement occurs, if the expected rate of increase of prices is less than the discount rate, given savings in real resources will have smaller and smaller present values the farther off they are. Consequently, a programme of fast exploitation will appear to yield greater aggregate resource savings than a slower programme. Furthermore, the implicit discount rate actually applied by governments in making decisions, which is to be distinguished from the discount rate used by civil servants and temporary economic advisers making apparently scientific calculations, may be very high because of the short time-horizon of government. In the 1960s and early 1970s, North Sea gas and oil held out the prospect of substantial balance-of-payments savings, which a government would naturally prefer to gain for itself rather than bequeath to successors (possibly of another party). There are some further comments later in this chapter (pages 43–4) and in Chapter 9 on the effects of government time-horizons on depletion policy.

By the early 1970s, although government time-horizons may have remained short, the rapid exploitation policy was beginning to be called in question because of changing views about future energy prices. Price expectations had begun to alter from about 1970 onwards, as concern about future energy shortage grew, and the drastic use by OPEC members of their semi-monopoly power between October 1973 and January 1975 caused a radical revision of expectations. Just as the previous popular view had been that oil prices would decline into the indefinite future, the idea now took hold that oil prices would rise for ever – or rather, until the exhaustion of resources in the not far distant future.[22] Whether or not such a turnround in expectations was justified, in these conditions there must have appeared to be some case for making one's resource savings in the more distant (higher-price) future.

In addition to the influence of changed price expectations on government decision-making, another important factor leading to reconsideration of the rapid exploitation policy was the substantial increase in estimates of the United Kingdom's oil and gas reserves. The rapid exploitation policy was initiated when only comparatively small natural gas reserves had been discovered. The 1967 Fuel Policy White Paper[23] points out that the target of 4000 million cfd of natural gas in 1975 would be equivalent to only about 15 per cent of expected United Kingdom energy demand in that year. As large oil finds were made from 1969 onwards,[24] it became clear, however, that by about 1980 oil supplies from the North Sea might well be sufficient to eliminate net imports of crude oil although there would be still some imports of relatively heavy crude oil, balanced by exports of light North Sea oil, in order to meet the United Kingdom's pattern of oil product demand. A memorandum from the Department of Trade and Industry to the Public Accounts Committee of the House of Commons at the end of 1972[25] already put 1980 oil production from the United Kingdom's part of the North Sea at 75 million tonnes; and by May 1975 the British Government's annual Brown Book[26] had raised the estimate to 100 to 130 million tonnes – that is, of the same order of magnitude as the output of Kuwait, Nigeria or Iraq in 1974. It was estimated that by the early 1980s annual production would be in the range of 100 to 150 million tonnes, which compared with the Government's forecast of oil demand in Britain at some 120 million tonnes per annum.[27] Recoverable oil reserves (proved, probable and possible) were assessed in the 1975 Brown Book as in the range 3000 to 4500 million tonnes, including areas designated but not licensed.

This big increase in petroleum reserves, especially given the rising price expectations mentioned earlier, was likely to lead to an examination of whether it would be better to spread future oil output over a longer period. Given the larger size of reserves it might appear possible to achieve considerable gains in security of supply and to the balance of payments while still producing a smaller percentage of reserves each year than had previously been anticipated. Although the United Kingdom seemed destined to be a price-taker in the world oil market (unless it decided to join OPEC), so that it was unlikely to be able to influence price significantly by holding back output, the expected price trend held out the possibility that, within limits, a slower rate of depletion than previously planned would lead to increased resource savings.

A third reason why the need for rapid exploitation seemed less pressing may have been that the Government no longer felt it so necessary to keep the oil companies happy. It has already been pointed out that rapid depletion of gas reserves was probably necessary to achieve such a low price in the first North Sea gas contracts, but by the mid-1970s the large gas fields in the southern North Sea had all achieved plateaux; in any case, there seems to have been no suggestion of attempting to reduce their depletion rates. For oil there was no sole buyer so there was no need to agree to rapid depletion as a 'sweetener' for low prices. The huge increase in OPEC oil prices initially raised substantially the apparent profitability of North Sea oil, and, although cost and tax increases quickly eroded much of the improvement, it may well have appeared to the Government that some form of power to control depletion could be introduced without seriously affecting the attractiveness of North Sea oil. Anyway, the need to encourage exploration probably seemed less urgent, since such large reserves had already been discovered.

Whether the reasons suggested above were the true ones is a matter of speculation. Possibly the change of view about depletion was as much the result of emotional reaction to an apparently very uncertain world energy market as to any systematic analysis of the situation. Whatever the reasons, the introduction of some kind of power to control depletion was not a matter of dispute between the two major political parties, although the regulatory method would have differed under the Conservatives and the controls were no doubt introduced earlier by a Labour Government committed to a significant increase in state intervention.

NORWAY'S DEPLETION POLICY

The depletion policy adopted by Norway – the other European country with large proved offshore oil and gas reserves – provides an interesting contrast to British policy in the 1960s and early 1970s. While Britain's objective was rapid exploitation, Norwegian governments from the beginning adopted a so-called 'go-slow' policy. This does not appear to mean that there were government-imposed restrictions on the depletion rates of fields already discovered: the go-slow took the form of limiting the issue of licences. In other words it was a policy of not allowing too many discoveries to be made.

In the first Norwegian licensing round in 1965, when interest was primarily in the southern parts of the North Sea, a much smaller area was licensed than in the first British round in 1964. Norway licensed seventy-eight blocks, compared with the first British award of 348 (although the Norwegian blocks are about twice the size of the British). Thereafter, Norwegian licensing policy seems to have become very restrictive.

The second round did not come until 1969 (whereas the British second round was in 1965) and only fourteen blocks were then allocated. An interim licence was awarded in 1971 to the Petronord group and the Norwegian Government was effectively forced in 1973 to give another interim licence to a Mobil/Statoil group in order to establish an interest in the portion of the Brent reservoir which appeared to lie on the Norwegian side of the median line.

The third full round of licensing took place in November 1974 when a mere eight blocks were allocated.[28] In addition nine blocks along the median line were selected and reserved so that Statoil could prepare development plans for them; the intention seems to have been that these blocks would be exploited by Statoil in collaboration with private companies. During 1976 several blocks along the Norwegian/British median line were allocated. The next full licensing round was due to take place late in 1977, when the Norwegian Government evidently originally intended to allocate fifteen blocks. However, a blowout on the Ekofisk field in April 1977, which resulted in an oil spillage of 10,000–12,000 tonnes, greatly increased concern about the effects of oil production on the fishing industry and the environment in general so that by mid-1977 there was considerable doubt about the future of oil exploration in the Norwegian sector. Before the blowout it had been intended to begin drilling in the area north of the 62nd Parallel in 1978 but it seems likely that there will be still further delays to the already much-postponed exploration of the northern Norwegian offshore.[29]

Some possible explanations for the differences between Norwegian and British exploitation policies are not hard to find. For example, there is a great difference in the relative sizes of the two countries' economies.[30] The United Kingdom's national income is about eight times that of Norway. British energy consumption of over 300 million tonnes coal equivalent (United Nations basis) compares with Norwegian consumption of less than 20 million tonnes coal equivalent. Oil consumption of about 90 million tonnes a year in the United Kingdom compares with about 8 million tonnes in Norway. By comparison with most developed countries, Norway has a large proportion of her energy consumption (some 40 per cent) supplied by indigenous production of hydro-electricity. Reserves already discovered in the Norwegian offshore area, which appear to be comparable to British offshore oil and gas reserves, are more than sufficient to support the gas and oil output of 70–75 million tonnes of oil equivalent per annum which is likely in the mid 1980s, given a continuation of the go-slow policy.[31] Output at this rate – mostly from Ekofisk, Statfjord and Frigg – would, of course, largely be exported. Because of the small size of the Norwegian economy, relative to potential North Sea production, the apparent advantages of rapid exploitation in terms of balance-of-payments savings and improved security of supply which British governments were so anxious to grasp no doubt seemed of much less significance to the Norwegian Government.

Indeed, rapid exploitation appears to have been seen by the Norwegian Government as positively disadvantageous because of its expected impact on the economic and social life of the country. It seems to have feared an inflationary effect on an already fully employed economy, disruption of the social structure, an adverse impact on the environment, and more specifically, damage to traditional industries such as fishing. In effect, the Government foresaw what it believed would be excessive external costs from rapid exploitation and decided that these costs should not be incurred. So far as one can tell, this government view reflected majority public opinion. Given the potential size of the North Sea sector relative to its economy, with a 'British rate' of exploitation Norway might have encountered similar problems of absorbing greatly increased government revenues to those experienced by some OPEC members since the October 1973 oil price increase, although Norway is of course a much more developed country and much less dependent on oil than the OPEC countries.

For such reasons, the Norwegian Government has exercised much tighter control over offshore development than have British governments and there has been a much closer association between North Sea policy and regional policy than in Britain. Detailed supervision of offshore exploitation runs right through the Norwegian system. The Ministry of Industry carefully vets all applicants for licences and selects those it regards as worthy on technical and commercial grounds. The Ministry's Petroleum Directorate supervises the activities of the licensees and the Norwegian state oil company, Statoil, has been given a large interest in Norwegian offshore operations. Statoil has 50 per cent shares in the Statfjord and Frigg fields and will have at least 50 per cent participation in discoveries made under licences issued from 1975 onwards. Norsk Hydro (51 per cent state-owned) also has some North Sea interests – for instance about one third of the Norwegian sector of Frigg.

Whether the Norwegian policy towards exploitation is better or worse than British policy is not our principal concern here. Certainly one can see significant differences between the economic and the social circumstances of the two countries which might justify different attitudes towards development. No one in Britain, except for the Scottish Nationalists, seems prepared to argue for a Norwegian-type go-slow. Such a policy in Britain would mean substantial delays to field development plans, given the large number of finds already made, and not just restrictive licensing. The Norwegians seem to have formulated a policy which they believe to be manageable without excessive social and economic disruption and to implement that policy they have imposed extensive and detailed state control. Most likely they will succeed in reducing social and economic change. But in the process they will incur costs.

If, for example, the world price of crude oil were to rise only slowly or to fall in the 1980s, the Norwegians would lose some of the benefits they could have had from earlier production. During the period when the major Norwegian sector discoveries were made – from the finding of Ekofisk in 1969 to the present – the prospects have appeared to be for substantial appreciation in the price of crude oil at a rate in excess of forgone interest and this may have prompted the Norwegian Government to believe, like the members of OPEC, that oil in the ground is a preferable investment to money in the bank. It remains to be seen whether the Norwegian Government's attitude towards exploitation would survive a period when oil prices were expected to fall or when balance-of-payments problems appeared.

Another possible future cost, which does not seem particularly important at present, is that the high degree of central control of the Norwegian sector has minimised the role of the private oil companies operating in Norway. At present this hardly matters to the Government, since it wants slow development and can afford to pick and choose its partners, but no one can be sure how long this situation will persist.

There are also more general doubts about the effects of a high degree of state control of oil and gas development which are set out in the last part of this chapter.

PETROLEUM AND SUBMARINE PIPELINES ACT, 1975

The statement about depletion control in the British Government's July 1974 White Paper, along with the other regulatory measures there proposed, led to various expressions of concern by the oil industry. For example, A. W. Pearce, chairman of the Esso Petroleum Company, said that government regulation of production rates would introduce considerable uncertainty into field development plans, and that if fields were to be forced to operate below capacity exploration effort would be discouraged.[32] While views about depletion control no doubt differed among the companies, they do not seem generally to have objected to the *principle* of some form of government control. After all many governments of oil-producing countries have such powers. In a memorandum to the Select Committee on Nationalised Industries in December 1974,[33] British Petroleum actually proposed the establishment of a 'regulatory commission', independent of the Department of Energy, which, *inter alia*, would be charged with conservation policies and with *pro rationing* where necessary. The main worry of the companies appears to have been the apparently sweeping powers implied by the phrase 'to control the level of production in the national interest'. Jesse Wyllie, president of Gulf Oil (Eastern Hemisphere), probably expressed a widely felt concern when he said 'nothing could be more disruptive than arbitrarily decreed reductions in planned rates'.[34] The companies seem to have feared that fields developed at considerable cost might be subjected to controls for purely short-term reasons.

By the end of the year, after consultations with the companies, Mr Varley, as Secretary of State for Energy, made a statement[35] which was evidently intended to reassure them by placing limits on the exercise of the British Government's power to regulate depletion. He said that oil companies and banks could take it that 'depletion policy and its implementation will not undermine the basis on which they have made plans and entered into commitments'. Although the Government could not define its long-term production policy before any oil had been produced and while large areas remained unexplored, reserve powers to control depletion in the future seemed necessary to 'ensure that this vital natural resource will be used at a rate which secures the greatest long-term benefit to the nation's economy'.

Government policy was still to allow rapid development to proceed up to about 1980, but regulation of production might then become necessary: 'How and when such powers may be used in the 1980s and 1990s will depend on the extent of the total funds [*sic*], on the world oil market and on the demand for energy. On all these points great uncertainty prevails.' Mr Varley said that *for the Celtic Sea* the depletion regime was still not settled: there the British National Oil Corporation might be used to establish fields in areas yet to be licensed 'whose reserves could be husbanded or developed quickly in accordance with the widest national interest'.

Mr Varley said government depletion policy would be based on the following guidelines:

(1) *Finds made before end-1975 under existing licences*: No delays would be imposed on development plans. Any production controls would not be applied before 1982 or four years after the start of production, whichever is later.

(2) *Finds made after end-1975 under existing licences*: No production cuts would be made before 150 per cent of investment in the field had been recovered.

(3) *All finds made after end-1975* [*presumably under old or new licences*]: Development delays would only be imposed after 'full consultation with the companies concerned so that premature investment is avoided'.

(4) *General*: Any use by the Government of depletion controls would recognise 'technical and commercial aspects of the fields in question' which would generally mean production cuts of no more than 20 per cent. The industry would be consulted on the necessary period of notice before cuts became effective. The Government would

also 'take into account the needs of the offshore supply industry' in the United Kingdom in considering development delays or production cuts.

The spirit of these reassuring words, however, does not seem to have found its way into the Petroleum and Submarine Pipelines Bill, published in April 1975, which set out a ministerial power to control depletion subject to virtually no constraints. The necessary authority was to be granted to the Minister under revised 'model clauses' which would apply both to production licences originally granted under the earlier Petroleum (Production) Regulations and to new licences. The new model clauses (15 and 16 in Schedule 2 of the Bill) gave the Minister effectively unlimited power to vary production plans and to set maximum and/or minimum production rates: he merely had to allow the licensee to make representations and then had to be satisfied that his decision is in the 'national interest'. Nor were there constraints on his ability to alter production rates since he could 'specify any rate by reference to such factors as the Minister thinks fit'. On the face of it, the Minister could determine any output rate he wanted and there was no provision for appeal from his decision.[36]

Although the companies seem to have been assured that the Varley guidelines remained operative, the form of the proposed legislation must have made them uncertain whether the safeguards would be observed in the long term. Clearly, the incorporation of such general statements in the necessary legal form might have raised problems.[37] The companies, however, appear to have been particularly concerned that there were no specific arbitration provisions to protect against arbitrary ministerial action.[38]

During the passage of the Bill through Parliament some of the oil industry's objections to the form of the legislation seem to have been taken into account. Model clause 16, which in the original version of the Bill had given the Minister power to specify maximum and minimum production rates, disappeared at the Commons Committee stage, but amended clauses 15 and 16 seem to contain all the powers necessary for the Minister to control production rates. The Petroleum and Submarine Pipelines Act, which received the Royal Assent in November 1975, gives the Minister power to approve, modify or reject programmes submitted by producers, which must specify their capital investment plans and propose maximum and minimum annual production rates for oil and gas. The Minister can reject programmes either on the grounds that they are contrary to 'good oilfield practice' or that production plans are not in the 'national interest'; producers then have to modify their proposals.

Furthermore, when the Minister approves a development programme he can give the producer a 'limitation notice' which specifies limits within which the Minister can, by means of a 'further notice' issued after some specified future period, direct him to produce. A further notice can require an increase in output compared with the producer's plans (provided the necessary expenditure is less than the cost of drilling a new well) if there is a 'national emergency', or a reduction in output if the Minister is satisfied that this would be in the 'national interest'.

From the producers' viewpoint, the new proposals have advantages in that the Government has to give advance notice of its intention to vary production and must specify limits. In effect, the producer has a guaranteed floor rate of production and the Minister's power to force him to increase output is restricted by the 'one new well' provision. Consequently the producer has less uncertainty than under the open-ended powers in the original version of the Bill.

The details, however, of limitation notices and further notices (such as maximum and minimum output rates and notice periods) are in the end at ministerial discretion. Quantities and periods are to be set 'by reference to such factors as the Minister thinks fit' provided he has listened to representations from the producer concerned. Although there have been some reports that the amended Bill contains an arbitration provision relevant to depletion control, inspection shows that this applies only to ministerial decisions about matters of good oilfield practice. The Minister still has absolute power to determine 'what is, is not, or is required in the national interest' and 'what is, or is required by reason of, a national emergency'. Paragraph 5(c) (ii) of model clause 15 makes it clear that ministerial decisions about what is in the national interest cannot be overridden by considerations of good oilfield practice.

Summarising, the Petroleum and Submarine Pipelines Act gives the Minister extensive power to control depletion rates. Apart from the good oilfield practice provision, which must be regarded as essential in this kind of legislation, he can make producers modify their development plans by pleading 'national interest' considerations. Subsequently he can modify the plans originally approved upwards ('national emergency') or downwards ('national interest') within limits and on notice which he determines, but which he must reveal to the producers in advance.

In addition to the Petroleum and Submarine Pipelines Act there are certain other means available to the United Kingdom Government of regulating North Sea output. First, it is, of course, possible to vary the issue of production licences so as to slow down or speed up the future rate of offshore output: the intention from 1977 onwards seems to be to issue smaller numbers of licences more regularly than in the past. Second, the 51 per cent state share in licences (exercised primarily through the British National Oil Corporation) might at some stage be used to influence depletion policy. Third, there are some very sweeping powers contained in the Energy Act of 1976 which gives the Secretary of

State for Energy authority to regulate output and prices of oil and natural gas if there is an 'actual or threatened [fuel] emergency' or if control is necessary to fulfil European Community or International Energy Agency obligations, or indeed if he simply believes that there is a need for energy 'conservation'. The Energy Bill as originally introduced covered a very wide range of issues and seems to have been a singularly ill-prepared piece of legislation. Although it was substantially improved during its passage through Parliament, parts of it may well be inconsistent with the Petroleum and Submarine Pipelines Act and with the Varley guidelines. For instance, it is not certain whether the 'one new well' limitation on the Minister's power to compel an output increase would be operative in the case of an emergency declared under the Energy Act and it appears that the 'Varley guidelines' need not apply if oil and gas supplies were to be controlled under the provisions of the Energy Act.[39]

DEPLETION CONTROL IN THEORY AND PRACTICE

It is probably true to say that by 1975 the principle of government depletion control was not a real issue in the United Kingdom. Both the Conservative Party and the oil companies objected to the Labour Government's proposed *mechanism* of regulation, as set out in the July 1974 White Paper and later in the Petroleum and Submarine Pipelines Bill, but Mr Varley's reassurances and the amendments made to the Bill in Parliament seem to have quietened some of their fears. It would, indeed, be difficult to argue against there being some government reserve power to control depletion, should the need arise, provided there are safeguards against arbitrary ministerial action. Most economists would accept that it is possible for circumstances to arise in which a government can justifiably intervene to alter company production programmes.

Some formidable difficulties, however, stand in the way of successful intervention. Briefly, these are of two kinds. First, it is an open question whether, at any given time, government can even identify in *which direction* company programmes should be varied, let alone whether it can determine such an elusive quantity as the optimal depletion rate for society, the criteria for establishing which are by no means obvious. A common assumption at present is that, outside times of 'national emergency', regulations should act to *reduce* company depletion rates: the July 1974 White Paper specifically mentions such reductions.[40] But, as will be shown below, there is no clear evidence that company depletion rates will invariably be super-optimal for society. Thus, if the direction of change is not obvious, one must consider the possibility that government intervention will move the depletion rate farther from its optimum than it would have been under producer control. Second, there are imperfections in the political process, which mean that one cannot assume that central intervention will be practised by textbook governments omniscient and intent only on disinterested promotion of the public good.

Regulation of depletion, whilst it has been operated in many countries, is not the simple matter which those who participated in the Parliamentary debates on the Petroleum and Submarine Pipelines Bill seem to have imagined. There are some practical difficulties in applying a regulatory system, such as that now instituted in Britain, which are considered in Chapter 7. In the rest of this chapter there is a more detailed examination of the theoretical issues of whether or not producer-determined depletion rates are likely to diverge from the optimum and some of the practical matters involved in government depletion control.

THEORY OF RESOURCE DEPLETION

First, consider how the individual producer will determine how to exploit a given stock of some non-renewable resource, such as oil, in the absence of any government restraints.[41] Assume that a company has an oil reserve of known size (Q) which is capable of being extracted at varying rates over time $(q_t, q_{t+1}, \ldots \ldots q_{t+n})$. q will be subject to upper and lower limits in any given year which will be set by extraction technology. Assume that Q is a *recoverable* reserve and so avoid the qualification which would have to be made in practice that Q is a partial function of the rate of extraction (q). The producer then faces an investment decision in the sense that in any period of time he has to decide, within the given technical limits, how much to invest in oil (that is, how much oil to leave in the ground) and how much to disinvest (that is, to extract).

His reasoning might be as follows. If the oil is extracted and sold, revenue is obtained which can be used for investment elsewhere and must therefore be expected to yield some positive return. If it is held in the ground this return (presumably measured approximately by the producer's rate of discount) is forgone but the oil in the ground may yield a return if it appreciates in value faster than costs of production — that is, if its price net of costs and taxes is rising. Whether or not a producer decides to produce a given quantity of oil in a given year therefore depends essentially on whether he believes the rate of net price appreciation (the opportunity cost of production) will exceed his rate of discount (the opportunity cost of not producing). If oil is kept in the ground the only return can be from net price appreciation; if it is produced, a return equal to the rate of discount can be earned.

Consequently a producer will be in equilibrium when he has so adjusted the distribution of output through time that his expected rate of net price appreciation ($\dot{p}$) equals his discount rate (i). [42]

If $\dot{p} \neq i$, the producer has an incentive to move output from one time-period to another, so as to increase his expected net present value (NPV), until equality is achieved. If $\dot{p} > i$, it will pay him to reduce output in the near term since expected price appreciation will more than compensate for forgone interest. If $\dot{p} < i$, there will be a tendency to increase output as other investment opportunities are perceived to be superior to investment in oil in the ground. Only when $\dot{p} = i$ is the producer maximising NPV at his rate of discount; the marginal barrel of oil will then be expected to earn the same whether it is extracted or held in the ground and the producer will be indifferent between the two courses of action. The expected NPV of a marginal barrel of oil will be the same whether it is produced in 1975, 1980 or 1990.

An explicit statement of such a policy of comparing prospective price appreciation with interest rates was made by Per Kleppe, the Norwegian Finance Minister. The *Financial Times* of 13 November 1975 reported Mr Kleppe as saying to a conference of economists: 'As long as some of Norway's petroleum reserves remained below the North Sea, their assets were "probably fairly well placed". A gradual rise in the relative price of petroleum would represent interest earned on these untouched assets. Reasoning along these lines, this kind of investment compares favourably with financial investment abroad.'

There have been similar statements from Middle East oil producers and other members of OPEC, which suggest that they have been influenced by the kind of depletion model discussed above. Indeed, as explained in Chapter 1, the most significant feature of the international oil market in the early 1970s, which led to the upward price trend between 1970 and 1973 and then to the massive price increases of 1973–75, seems to have been the generation of expectations of substantial price increases in the future. The oil producers of OPEC appear to have been strongly affected, consciously or not, by the then widespread discussion of future shortages of resources (including oil). In the circumstances they naturally drew the conclusion that scarcity, or fear of scarcity, would result in sharply rising prices – in contrast to the 1960s when prices tended to decline – so that the appropriate action for a producer of oil was to reduce planned levels of output, thus conserving resources in anticipation of higher prices.

In addition to this apparent increase in $\dot{p}$, i also seems to have declined at about the same time (see Chapter 1, pages 8–9). As the producing governments took control of output decisions from the oil companies in the 1970s there was a tendency for the discount rates which determined production policy to fall. Though it is extremely difficult to conduct rigorous empirical tests of theories based on expectations, the hypothesis that it was a rise in $\dot{p}$ relative to i which was behind the fundamental change in the oil market in the early 1970s seems to have a great deal of explanatory power, though there were also political changes which reinforced the influence of the economic variables.

The $\dot{p} = i$ equilibrium condition holds whatever the market form, provided the producer is a maximiser of expected NPV.[43] Nevertheless, the way in which the equilibrium is obtained will, of course, vary with the market form. With given extraction technology and given Q, the three significant variables to the producer are $\dot{p}$, q and i. Of these i can be regarded as normally uncontrollable by the producer, since it will be primarily a function of market rates of interest, and q will be a policy instrument since the producer is taken to be free to determine his depletion rate. However, $\dot{p}$ is more complex. The cost component, which includes taxes and royalties, is partly controlled by the producer but is outside his influence to the extent that it depends on general cost movements and government tax policy. The other component – the market price of oil – will be an uncontrollable variable in a highly competitive market, but will come nearer to a policy instrument, with a trade-off against q, as the market approaches monopoly.

Although, from the producer's point of view, the $\dot{p} = i$ equilibrium condition is independent of the degree of competition in the market in which he operates, the state of competition may, of course, make a considerable difference to the social desirability of the depletion rate which emerges. The standard argument is that a perfectly competitive market, provided external costs and benefits are internalised, would automatically lead to an optimal depletion rate for society. Perfect competition might appear to lead to an optimal distribution of resources over time – that is, during present and succeeding generations – as well as to optimal distribution at any given time.

MARKET IMPERFECTIONS AND THE RATE OF DEPLETION

The analysis above suggests one way of approaching the question of whether or not it is possible to determine an optimum depletion rate for North Sea oil. If the perfectly competitive market, in addition to its other apparent virtues, would lead to optimum depletion over time, the conventional economists' method of determining whether or not optimum depletion will appear without government intervention is to investigate whether or not so-called market 'imperfections' and market failures exist. This approach has difficulties of its own which will be considered later – for instance, one must have doubts about using such an idealised model when virtually all actual experience is of 'imperfections', and in any case the optimisation provided by perfect competition is of a very restricted nature – but it will be followed for the time being to see if it sheds any light on the problem. Some of the possible market imperfections which might affect North Sea oil depletion are listed below and are discussed briefly.

MONOPOLISTIC ELEMENTS

The presence of some degree of monopoly is a market imperfection which one would expect to cause divergence of the depletion rate from the optimum. A monopolist engaged in maximising net present value would tend to raise price and restrict output, compared with the outcome of a perfectly competitive market, and consequently it would seem that the presence of monopoly would result in a sub-optimal rate of resource depletion. [44] But it is not so clear that this would be the effect in the real world. This is partly for the well-known reason that predictions of the relative behaviour of firms in perfect competition and monopoly are fraught with difficulty since costs as well as demand may be a function of the degree of competition, the objectives of firms may not be the same in the two markets, and rates of technical progress may also differ.

Another reason for doubt about the direction of divergence from optimality under monopoly is that the price elasticity of demand for the 'monopolist's' product may change over time, and the demand for his product may shift. The most likely case is one in which the demand curve shifts to the left over time and demand becomes more elastic at any given price as substitutes are developed for the product. For example, OPEC has a high degree of monopoly power at present: the oil producers have taken advantage of the current inelasticity of demand by restricting output and raising price, thereby generating expectations of further price increases which in turn have increased their incentive to hold oil in the ground. However, if substitutes for OPEC oil are seen to be under development, so that at a given date in the future and at a given price the demand for OPEC oil appears likely to be less than had previously been expected, then price expectations may well be revised downwards. That is, $\dot{p}$ may fall relative to i, thus making it attractive to speed up the rate of exploitation. If oil producers are risk-averse, the element of uncertainty induced by the perception that substitutes are on their way might cause a particularly substantial increase in the rate of depletion. As output then rose, $\dot{p}$ might conceivably become negative as in the 1960s. [45] This kind of case — monopoly now but a long-term price ceiling in prospect because of increasing competition — would be likely to mean that sub-optimal depletion would not persist. One might judge that the depletion rate of world oil resources is at present below its competitive level because of the activities of OPEC, but that output might rise towards or beyond the optimum within a few years as monopoly power is eroded. [46]

The relevance of this to North Sea depletion is as follows. The individual North Sea producer has no significant monopoly power. He is, as explained in Chapter 1, a price-taker in a market dominated by the members of OPEC, who set prices. Nor would the British North Sea producers as a whole have substantial market power if they were to attempt to exploit the market.[47] Consequently, the answer to the question of whether or not monopolistic elements are causing non-optimal depletion of the North Sea turns on the presence of monopoly in the *world* oil market rather than in the North Sea. Therefore, one might tentatively conclude on the basis of this discussion of OPEC that, with other things equal (implying the unrealistic assumption of neutral government policy towards exploitation) and subject to the qualifications mentioned earlier, monopoly might at present be causing *slower* depletion of the North Sea than would have occurred under perfect competition. But the effects of dynamic market forces in changing price expectations may well so temper the power of OPEC in the next few years that the natural reaction of oil producers the world over will be to increase their rates of exploitation. Whether or not changing price expectations would result in super-optimal depletion is very hard to foresee.

POLLUTION

An obvious market failure, although one not always considered by economists in the context of natural resource depletion, is that costs and prices in the market will not normally reflect in full the effects of pollution of the natural environment. Furthermore, there has been a general failure by governments to internalise the costs of pollution. Whilst there has been progress in recent years in setting standards and levying charges, it would generally be agreed that the system is still far from one in which the full costs of pollution enter into decision-making. There are difficulties of many kinds which make a world of internalised pollution costs difficult to envisage – a lack of scientific knowledge of what is pollution and what is not, problems of devising charges and enforcing them and so on – but the aim here is merely to enquire about the likely effects on energy depletion of the present system.

Since the production, transportation and consumption of fuels have a substantial and generally adverse effect on the environment (through emissions to air and water, visual disamenities and all the potential problems of nuclear fission power), it follows that fuels are on the whole under-priced compared with a system in which prices incorporate social costs. One can argue, therefore, that in the world energy market as a whole, other things being equal, energy resources are being depleted too fast.[48] It might appear on the same grounds that the rates of depletion of North Sea oil and gas are too high.

It is not so obvious that pollution externalities are raising the depletion rates for North Sea oil and gas above the competitive optimum. One of the effects of the internalisation of pollution costs would almost certainly be to raise energy prices compared with prices in general, but it would also probably change energy prices relative to one another. For example, (i) natural gas is a relatively non-polluting energy source, the price of which might well decline relative to other fuels with the introduction of a system of pollution charges; (ii) oil is perhaps 'cleaner' than coal and might fall in price relative to the latter; whereas (iii) electricity from nuclear fission might become somewhat more expensive (though this is a contentious matter) if its environmental costs were incorporated in its price. At present there is not sufficient knowledge to determine *either* what the effects on relative fuel prices would be if the costs of pollution were fully borne by the producers *or* what the price-elasticities of demand would turn out to be in those circumstances. It is by no means inconceivable, however, that British offshore natural gas reserves would be depleted more rapidly, although the rate of oil exploitation might be reduced.

EXCESSIVE INTEREST RATES

A common argument is that market interest rates tend to exceed social time-preference rates because market rates reflect risks to individuals which cancel out for society as a whole, since they incorporate taxes which are transfers within society, and because of a general thoughtlessness about future generations (so-called Pigovian myopia). If market interest rates are indeed excessive, i will be increased relative to p and there will be a tendency, compared with a perfectly competitive market in which market rates equal the social rate of time preference, for resources to be depleted too rapidly. In other words, high interest rates will discourage investment in resources in the ground.

The logical conclusion of this argument is that *all* investment – not only non-renewable resources, but in buildings, plant and equipment as well – will be too low.[49] That is, not only is one generation leaving too little to the next in the form of natural resources, but also too little by way of capital equipment and (probably) associated technological advance. Thus if interest rates were to be reduced this would presumably stimulate all forms of productive investment, the rate of increase of real gross national product (GNP) would rise and, *ceteris paribus*, non-renewable resources would be depleted more rapidly. In other words, the world's natural resources would be transformed into man-made capital at a faster rate and, at the margin, more of this capital and less natural resources would be bequeathed to future generations.

One cannot, therefore, draw simple conclusions about the impact of interest rates on resource investment without considering their effect on other forms of investment and the feedback to the resource market.

Moreover, in the case of the United Kingdom the empirical evidence is by no means clear that future generations are being starved of natural resources by reason of excessively high interest rates. Real interest rates in the United Kingdom in the mid-1970s have been generally negative even before tax. As an example of the level and the trend of real interest rates we can compare the flat yield on $2\frac{1}{2}$ per cent consols with the annual rate of change in the retail price index: Table 2.2 below shows that on this definition of real long-term rates, they appear in the mid-1970s to be well below zero and they have not been above 2 per cent since 1970. The 1970s might be regarded as abnormal, but even in the 1950s and 1960s there appears to be little support for the view that the United Kingdom discounts the future heavily.

TABLE 2.2 Money and Real Long-term Rates of Interest in the United Kingdom (percentage)

	Yield on $2\frac{1}{2}\%$ consols (1)	Change in retail price index versus previous year (2)	Approximate implied real long-term rate of interest (3)
1950	3.5	+ 3.4	+ 0.1
1955	4.2	+ 5.3	− 1.1
1960	5.4	+ 0.1	+ 5.3
1965	6.4	+ 4.7	+ 1.6
1970	9.2	+ 6.4	+ 2.6
1971	9.1	+ 9.4	− 0.3
1972	9.1	+ 7.1	+ 1.9
1973	10.9	+ 9.2	+ 1.5
1974	15.0	+ 16.1	− 0.9
1975	14.7	+ 24.2	− 7.6
1976	14.2	+ 16.5	− 2.0

SOURCE *The British Economy, Key Statistics 1900–1970* (London: London and Cambridge Economic Service and *The Times*, 1971); and *Monthly Digest of Statistics* (London: H.M. Stationery Office, various issues).

It is open to anyone to argue that proper concern for future generations *should* lead to even lower rates of interest, but this is a matter of judgement. The situation in the United Kingdom has for some years been a far cry from the high positive interest rates of which conservationists often complain.

Another possible imperfection in market interest rates is that the discount rates of private owners of resources may be increased because they expect expropriation by a government in the foreseeable future: thus depletion rates will be increased. It is, for instance, likely that in the 1960s the discount rates of the oil companies operating in the OPEC countries were higher than they would otherwise have been because the OPEC governments were expected to take over the companies' operations; consequently the companies discounted heavily any net revenues expected to accrue after the next few years.[50] This kind of imperfection, however, is a direct *result* of actual or expected government intervention and is therefore to be distinguished from the other imperfections so far discussed. The next section of this chapter returns to the imperfections of central intervention and to possible differences between company and government rates of discount.

FORECASTING PROBLEMS

Anyone familiar with the practice of how oil companies actually determine depletion profiles will no doubt have been shocked at the simplified nature of the $p = i$ model. Because of uncertainties about the environment in which a company operates and indeed uncertainties about its own objectives, optimising the depletion rate for a given field is inevitably an uneasy compromise between engineering and commercial factors with a large element of managerial judgement thrown in. It is much more a process of 'satisficing' than maximising. Companies may have objectives other than NPV maximisation, their attitudes towards risk vary (among different companies at a given time and for different managers of a given company over time) and may influence depletion profiles.

Future prices are very uncertain, as are the rates of discount which would be appropriate in future years: it is hard enough to assess what discount rate to use even for very short-term projects. The size of the reserves to be depleted is unlikely to be known at all accurately until after several years' production experience, and the interaction between production rates and eventual recovery of reserves may be unclear. A field development programme is thus a difficult exercise in forecasting and planning many years ahead, full of uncertainties about reservoir size and characteristics, costs, prices, interest rates, taxation and other aspects of government policy.[51]

Probably the only certain thing that can be said about the forecasts on which depletion plans must be based is that they will be wrong.[52] This being so, events will differ from expectations and this will, in itself, lead to non-optimised depletion. If a producer had known when planning his programme, what would actually happen to interest rates, prices, costs, government policy and the other variables on which the depletion rate depends, he would almost invariably have planned differently. In the perfectly competitive resource market it is normally assumed that optimality is achieved either through perfect foresight or through perfectly efficient forward and insurance markets.[53] Obviously, neither of these conditions applies in the cases of oil and gas, although there have been signs of the appearance of embryonic forward markets in crude oil.[54]

It must be concluded therefore that one of the inherent characteristics of the world – the presence of uncertainty – will lead to a depletion rate different from the perfectly competitive optimum. In which direction the depletion rate will diverge is, however, itself uncertain. There are some reasons why, *ceteris paribus*, under-depletion might occur – for example, 'early' estimates of oil and gas resources are quite frequently too low and producers may therefore initially deplete a field more slowly than if they had known actual reserves – but it would be difficult to make out a convincing general case for a tendency towards either under-depletion or over-depletion on account of incorrect forecasts.

PROBLEMS OF INTERVENTION

The most important feature of the above discussion of market imperfections is the absence of firm conclusions about the relationship between market rates of depletion and optimal rates. Some reasons why depletion rates for North Sea oil and gas might be sub-optimal are monopoly and reserve underestimation. Other reasons why super-optimal depletion might ensue are pollution externalities and 'excessive' interest rates. But in each case the arguments for sub- or super-optimality have to be qualified and in any event the presence of long-term forecasting problems makes it extremely hard to draw general conclusions about the direction of divergence from optimality. In other words, given all the uncertainties, it seems very unlikely that optimality is attainable except by chance. Furthermore, although this study has so far followed the convention of assuming that a Pareto optimal position should be the ideal there is no particular reason why this assumption should be made.[55]

To the extent that Pareto optimality is regarded as an automatic result of perfect competition with all external effects internalised, one must consider all the other consequences of a perfectly competitive world: an obvious problem in the case being considered is that there is a high probability that such a world would never have developed the technology to explore and exploit the North Sea. Therefore one naturally has qualms about using this definition of optimality in this case. Or if one says that Pareto optimality should be achieved by government intervention, one must consider, first, the difficulty if not impossibility of attaining the supposed result of perfect competition when one cannot clearly see what that result would be; and, second, the costs of intervention. Since enough has already been said to show the elusive nature of 'optimality', one can now examine the difficulties in the process of intervention. It would be inappropriate here to discuss the role of government intervention in detail, but some brief comments will be made both on the general question and on how it relates to North Sea depletion.

Economics in general, and welfare economics in particular, often suffer from a view of government which, though convenient for analytical purposes, is highly idealised. All too frequently one sees recommendations that 'imperfections' in the market should be remedied by central intervention which show no understanding of the imperfections in the intervention process itself and of the substantial costs it may bring. The *deus ex machina* view of government – as a body which can always be brought in at the appropriate time to clear up the wreckage left by the other actors – is so naive that it would hardly be worth a mention if it were not so influential. To some extent it is sheer wishful thinking. It would be so convenient if the imperfections of the world could be cleared away at zero cost. But life is not so simple.

The model of the world which seems to influence the views of many economists, politicians and civil servants can with little exaggeration be pictured as follows. There are essentially two important groupings in the economy. On the one hand are the ordinary mortals (or private sector) who are assumed to be motivated by self-interest of one form or another. On the other is a government group which is more far-sighted, more high-minded and less self-interested and which fixes its eyes firmly on the 'national interest'. The pursuit of self-interest by mortals in the market place cannot be relied upon to produce desirable results for society as a whole; for this to be achieved, disinterested intervention by the government group is necessary.

Once one departs from this naive model of the world the general case for government intervention tends to break down. If politicians and civil servants are also pursuing their personal interests,[56] there is no more reason to believe that the results of their actions will necessarily benefit society than there is for maintaining that the market will always achieve the social optimum.

Indeed, the pursuit of personal interest by civil servants and politicians might be regarded as inherently dangerous in the circumstances of the 1970s because of the concentration of power in the public sector as compared with the greater diffusion of interests in the private sector. Although the imperfections of the market system have been written about at enormous length, most of them have their parallels in the government system:

    (*a*) It is true, for example, that shareholders may not exercise very effective control over many large corporations, but it is also true that politicians are not easily controlled by the British electorate nor are they particularly responsive to its wishes. Civil servants who make many of the important decisions, *either* directly *or* by narrowing the range of alternatives presented to the politicians, may well be less controlled than most company managements.

(*b*) Then it is sometimes argued that private companies discount the future too heavily. But governments with an eye on the next election may have even higher discount rates. Consequently the general belief that government regulation will reduce the rate of depletion of North Sea resources may be false. Government control might, in practice, result in *faster* exploitation because of the desire of politicians to obtain benefits now rather than in the future.[57]

(c) Again, it is suggested that governments have better forecasting ability than private companies, whereas on the whole the evidence seems to point in the other direction — as one would expect, since good forecasting is primarily a matter of developing an understanding of a particular market.

(d) Monopoly in the market system can also have its parallel in over-powerful central governments which limit the freedom of their citizens. Indeed, a lengthier discussion of the costs of intervention would show this to be one of the major 'externalities' of government action. The British system in particular, with no explicit separation of powers and an executive subject only to infrequent and inefficient restraints through the electoral system and to international constraints, exhibits many of the characteristics of a monopoly which is increasing its power over time at the expense of the rest of the community.

CONCLUSIONS

To return to the depletion of North Sea oil and gas, while one may agree that it is sensible for a government to have a reserve power to control production, it should now be clear how many difficulties lie in the way of the use of that power so as to improve on the market outcome. Ministers will no doubt be prepared to set maximum and minimum production rates, to issue limitation notices and further notices, but on what bases will they do so? There is no way of knowing to what pressures they will be subject and what matters will be uppermost in their minds when they have to make these decisions. Perhaps, as Mr Varley said, they will at times look at the North Sea as a long-term prospect, or perhaps the opinion polls and the proximity of the next election will dominate their thoughts. Certainly one danger against which they will have to guard is that, unless production control is very carefully managed, it may well have all manner of unintended side-effects — such as the one mentioned earlier of increasing uncertainty among the producers (see pages 40–1), raising their discount rates and thereby accelerating depletion of the North Sea.

Perhaps the most important point one can make about depletion control is how very difficult it will be to apply successfully: at the least one can hope for a cautious attitude from the Government so as to avoid the huge and costly mistakes which can so easily accompany centralised decision-making. This chapter has inevitably been rather negative, since it is necessary to destroy some of the myths about depletion control – in particular, the absurd idea that a government has great gifts of foresight, wisdom and benevolence which make it both able and willing to operate an efficient control system. In Chapter 7 there is an analysis of the likely effects on producing companies of the British system of regulating output and in Chapter 9 there are some positive suggestions for a more open depletion policy than seems at present to be contemplated by the British Government. Before returning to the depletion control issue, however, some of the basic data about likely future oil supplies, the tax system and company profitability need to be examined: the next four chapters attempt to provide the necessary statistical basis.

NOTES AND REFERENCES

1. An earlier version of this chapter appeared in Robinson and Jon Morgan, *Economic Consequences of Controlling the Depletion of North Sea Oil and Gas*, Guest Paper No. 3 (London: Trade Policy Research Centre, 1976).
2. For comments on the establishment view, see Harry G. Johnson, 'What Passes for Economics in the English Establishment', *The Banker*, London, October 1975.
3. *United Kingdom Offshore Oil and Gas Policy*, Cmnd. 5696 (London: H.M. Stationery Office, 1964).
4. *North Sea Oil and Gas*, First Report from the Committee of Public Accounts, House of Commons, Session 1972–73 (London, H.M. Stationery Office, 1973) paragraph 96.
5. *Ibid.*, Minutes of Evidence, Qs 293–305.
6. *North Sea Oil and Gas, op. cit.*, discusses at length the British tax system for offshore oil and gas and makes comparisons with other countries.
7. Each set of regulations superseded the previous set, except for licences already granted; the changes made to the Regulations over time were relatively minor. A Memorandum by the Department of Trade and Industry in *North Sea Oil and Gas, op. cit.*, pp. 26–63 *et passim*, explains some of the legislative background.
8. See, for example, the Petroleum (Production) Regulations, 1964 and 1965, Section 3(1).
9. Details of the Gas Council's marketing plans are shown in their *Natural Gas in the Seventies*, July 1970, which forecast sales in 1974/5 as 13,530 million therms. Actual sales in 1974/5 were quite close to this at 12,932 million therms. See also Table 2.1.
10. *Fuel Policy*, White Paper, Cmnd. 3438 (London: H.M. Stationery Office, 1967) paragraph 95. See also its Appendix II, which explains the

policy of channelling natural gas primarily into 'premium' markets but allowing some 'bulk' use to enable rapid depletion.

11. The 'plateau' is the output achieved by a field after all production and transportation facilities have been installed. In the case of a North Sea gas field, it would normally be sustained for around ten years before production began to decline: the length of plateau for a North Sea oilfield would usually be much shorter. The 'build-up' period covers the years before the plateau is attained when production wells are being brought into use.

12. Total gas available in Great Britain from public supply in 1965 was 3752 million therms, or the equivalent of about 1030 million cfd of 1000 Btu natural gas.

13. Comments on price policy are in Kenneth W. Dam, *Oil Resources — Who Gets What How?* (Chicago: University of Chicago Press, 1976) chs 8–10, and Robinson, *Competition for Fuel* (London: Institute of Economic Affairs, 1971).

14. *North Sea Oil and Gas*, *op. cit.*, Minutes of Evidence, Q. 304.

15. *Financial Times*, London, 22 May 1974.

16. *Ibid.*, 28 May 1974. This compares with expected production on present plans of about 100 million tons a year in 1980 (see Chapters 1 and 3). Subsequently the Scottish Nationalists appear to have accepted that, since it is now almost certain that output will be over 100 million tons in the 1980s, the costs of restricting production would be high. According to Gordon Wilson (*Petroleum Review*, London, February 1977), beyond 1980 ' . . . the aim must be to bring down annual production to between 50 million and 80 million tons . . .'

17. *Financial Times*, 12 September 1974. The proposal was elaborated by Patrick Jenkin, then Opposition Spokesman on Energy, during the report stage of the Petroleum and Submarine Pipelines Bill, *Parliamentary Debates* [*Hansard*] (London: H.M. Stationery Office) (hereafter cited as *Hansard*), 28 July 1975, cols. 1301–12. Mr Jenkin had made clear in the second reading debate on the Bill, *Hansard*, 30 April 1975, cols. 503–8, that the Conservatives were not in principle opposed to depletion control though they objected to its retrospective application to existing licences.

18. *United Kingdom Offshore Oil and Gas Policy*, Cmnd. 5696 (London: H.M. Stationery Office, 1974).

19. One of the most influential was D. L. Meadows *et al.*, *The Limits to Growth*, Report for the Club of Rome (London: Earth Island, 1972). For comments on the effects of forecasts of energy shortages see Robinson, *The Energy Crisis and British Coal*, *op. cit.*, and also Robinson, *Energy Depletion and the Economics of OPEC*, *op. cit.*

20. The equilibrium conditions for a resource producer planning his output programme, which depend on the relationship between expected prices and his discount rate, are set out in the section on the Theory of Resource Depletion (pp. 34–6).

21. *North Sea Oil and Gas*, *op. cit.*, Minutes of Evidence, Qs 302–3. Sensitivity tests were made using higher and lower figures.

22. For a fuller explanation see Robinson, *Energy Depletion and the Economics of OPEC*, *op. cit.*, and 'The Depletion of Energy Resources' in Pearce (ed.), *op. cit.*

23. *Fuel Policy*, Cmnd. 3438 (London: H.M. Stationery Office, 1967) para. 96.

24. The first major oil find in the North Sea was Ekofisk in the Norwegian sector in 1969. The first large discovery in British waters was Forties in 1970.

25. *North Sea Oil and Gas, op. cit.*, Minutes of Evidence, 13 December 1972, Memorandum by the Department of Trade and Industry, p. 52.

26. *Development of the Oil and Gas Reserves of the United Kingdom* (London: Department of Energy, 1975).

27. The consumption forecast is in a Written Answer by Mr Varley, as Secretary of State for Energy, *Hansard*, 6 December 1974, col. 647. Some further comments by Mr Varley on offshore oil supplies and 'self-sufficiency' are in *Nationalised Industries and the Exploitation of North Sea Oil and Gas*, First Report from the Select Committee on Nationalised Industries, House of Commons Session 1974–75 (London: H.M. Stationery Office, 1975) Qs 636–41.

28. Information on the Norwegian licensing rounds is given in Dam, 'The Evolution of North Sea Licensing Policy in Britain and Norway', *Journal of Law and Economics*, Chicago, October 1974, and his *Oil Resources: Who Gets What How?, op. cit.* See also Report No. 81 to the Storting, Norwegian Ministry of Industry, Oslo, 1974–75.

29. See *The Petroleum Economist*, London, June 1977, pp. 239–40; *Financial Times*, 20 May 1977; and *Noroil*, Stavanger, May 1977, pp. 43–4.

30. National income, expressed in US$, is taken from *Yearbook of National Accounts Statistics 1975* (New York: United Nations, 1976) vol. iii, Table 182. The energy and oil statistics are from *World Energy Supplies 1950–74*, (New York: United Nations, 1976). For more details of the British and Norwegian energy markets see Ray and Robinson, *The European Energy Market in 1980* (London: Staniland Hall, 1975).

31. See *World Energy Outlook* (Paris: OECD, 1977) ch. II; *The Petroleum Economist*, London, January 1977, pp. 23–5, and May 1977, pp. 194–5; and *The Annual Report and Accounts of Statoil for 1976*, Stavanger, Norway, p. 8.

32. *The Petroleum Economist*, September 1974, p. 334.

33. *Nationalised Industries and the Exploitation of North Sea Oil and Gas, op. cit.*, pp. 106–7. The functions of the Commission are explained on p. 307 of the Report.

34. The *Sunday Times*, London, 22 September 1974.

35. *Hansard*, Written Answers, 6 December 1974, cols. 648–50.

36. The model clauses for production licences contained a general arbitration provision (clause 40) but this excludes matters which are expressly stated to be 'determined, decided, directed, approved or consented to by the Minister'.

37. For example, parliamentary draftsmen might well have found extreme difficulty in putting into unambiguous form statements which distinguish between development delays and production cuts. The latter are presumably intended to be output reductions, compared with company plans, after the 'plateau' has been reached. The final form of the Act seems to have attempted to provide a framework within which the Varley guidelines can be applied.

38. See Adrian Hamilton, 'In the Hands of the Government', *Financial Times*, 27 June 1975.
39. Morgan and Robinson, 'A Review of the Energy Act (1976)', forthcoming.
40. See the quotation from the 1967 Fuel Policy White Paper on p. 23. The provision to increase production in a national emergency, included in the amended Petroleum and Submarine Pipelines Act, is presumably intended to cope with events such as Arab oil restrictions or coalminers' strikes.
41. See Chapter I, pp. 8–9. The subsequent argument is developed at more length with reference to OPEC in Robinson, *Energy Depletion and the Economics of OPEC, op. cit.* An excellent summary of resource depletion theory is in R. M. Solow, 'The Economics of Resources or the Resources of Economics', *American Economic Review*, New York, May 1974. See also Pearce (ed.), *op. cit.*, and 'Symposium on the Economics of Exhaustible Resources', *Review of Economic Studies*, Cambridge, Mass., December 1974. An early statement of resource depletion theory is H. Hotelling, 'The Economics of Exhaustible Resources', *Journal of Political Economy*, Chicago, vol. 39, pp. 137–75.
42. It is assumed, for simplicity, that the producer has in mind a price *trend* rather than specific future prices for particular years. Similarly, it is assumed that he uses a single discount rate rather than different rates for different future years. Other complications ignored here, because they are not strictly relevant to the analysis, are exchange rate fluctuations (which would matter to an oil exporter) and the effects of inflation. As regards the latter, one would expect the producer to be concerned with the expected *real* price of oil and the *real* interest rate but provided the same price index is applied to oil prices and to interest rates it will make no difference whether the $\dot{p}$ versus i comparison is made in real or money terms.
43. Net present value maximisation may, however, be a less likely company objective outside reasonably competitive conditions. If the producer is not maximising net present value it is still likely that he will respond to differences between $\dot{p}$ and i in the way suggested.
44. See John Kay and James Mirlees, 'The Desirability of Natural Resource Depletion', in Pearce (ed.), *op. cit.*
45. See Robinson, *Energy Depletion and the Economics of OPEC, op. cit.*, and Robinson, 'The Depletion of Energy Resources', in Pearce (ed.), *op. cit.*
46. It is possible that OPEC's monopoly power will persist longer than suggested here because of actions by the oil-consuming countries. See Robinson, *Energy Depletion and the Economics of OPEC, op. cit.*
47. Of course, the United Kingdom could participate in the exercise of OPEC's market power by joining the Organisation, but this is not germane to the present discussion of whether there are now imperfections which lead away from the competitive market solution.
48. See Robinson, *Energy Depletion and the Economics of OPEC, op. cit.*
49. See Pearce (ed.), *op. cit.*, p. 163. Some further complications in the effects of interest rates on resource depletion are explored in R. L. Gordon, 'Conservation and the Theory of Exhaustible Resources', *Canadian Journal of Economics and Political Science*, Toronto, August 1966: and D. R. Lee and D. Orr, 'The Private Discount Rate and Resource "Conservation"', *ibid.*, August 1975.

50. These high discount rates seem to have been one of the contributory factors in the very large increase in OPEC oil output during the 1960s. See Chapter 1 and Robinson, *Energy Depletion and the Economics of OPEC, op. cit.*, pp. 14–20.

51. This is not to say that the results of company depletion planning will necessarily differ radically from those of the maximiser of expected net present value. It may well be that a producer's behaviour can be approximately captured by assuming that the results of his actions are *as if* he equated his expected rate of net price appreciation with his expected discount rate. At the least, if $p < i$ he is likely to increase production.

52. For further discussion of the problems of forecasting see Robinson, *Business Forecasting: an Economic Approach* (London: Nelson, 1971).

53. The effects of the absence of such markets are analysed in Geoffrey Heal, 'Economic Aspects of Natural Resource Depletion', in Pearce (ed.), *op. cit.*

54. See *The Petroleum Economist*, October 1974, pp. 364–6.

55. Some telling criticisms of the basis of Paretian welfare economics are made in Charles K. Rowley and Alan T. Peacock, *Welfare Economics: a Liberal Restatement* (London: Martin Robertson, 1975).

56. Anthony Downs, *An Economic Theory of Democracy* (New York: Harper & Row, 1957), especially ch. 15. See also Robinson and Paul Remington: 'The Formulation of Energy Policy', *Petroleum Review*, September/October 1976.

57. See Chapter 9 and Robinson and Morgan, 'Will North Sea Oil Save the British Economy?', *The Petroleum Economist*, January 1977, and 'The Supply of North Sea Oil', *The Chemical Engineer*, Rugby, June 1977.

CHAPTER 3

British North Sea Oil Supplies

In the short period during which the North Sea has been recognised as an important petroleum province, many changes have taken place in the environment in which the producing companies operate.[1] It has also become clear that there are considerable variations in the characteristics of the fields so far discovered; there is no such thing as a typical North Sea field and it is therefore rather hazardous to predict the nature of any future discoveries. No doubt the future holds many surprises so that one needs to be cautious about projecting North Sea supplies ahead. Much of this book is concerned with the effects on North Sea supplies and profitability of *changes* in the operating environment – for example, variations in taxes (Chapter 5), changes in prices (Chapter 6) and the imposition of government depletion control (Chapter 7).

The approach used here to the difficult problem of prediction is to take as a starting-point a 'surprise-free' projection of North Sea supplies up to the end of the century. This chapter sets out such a projection, which is intended to demonstrate approximately how one might expect North Sea oil output to change over time if the environment in which the companies operate remains much as it is now – if, for example, there are no major technological changes in exploration and production methods, the ratio between oil prices and exploitation costs does not alter significantly, tax rates and the tax system remain as now, and there is no government control of depletion rates. It is obvious that, in the future, surprises *will* very likely occur as they have always occurred in the past. The justification for starting from the surprise-free projection is that it provides a benchmark against which the impact of changes in key variables – as investigated in later chapters – can be judged. The rest of this chapter therefore examines the likely supply of North Sea oil up to the year 2000 from established fields, from probable developments of existing reserves and from discoveries which are assumed to be made in the future.

Any analysis of future North Sea oil supplies is bound to have wide error margins, especially when it looks ahead over twenty years. Even for an individual producing company, with relatively detailed information about the characteristics of one of its own finds, a decision to develop that discovery involves many technical, economic and political uncertainties. The outside observer, attempting to estimate future supplies from the North Sea as a whole at what is still an early stage in the exploitation of the area, can obviously only give a broad idea of what the future may hold.

Fortunately, there have been a number of events in the last few years which have made future output prospects from the British North Sea a little less difficult to assess. Continued exploration has helped to define the geology somewhat more clearly; better financing techniques for North Sea fields have come into use; the new tax system has been instituted; the Government's initial programme of increasing its control over offshore oil has been largely completed (although there may be tighter safety measures to come); some companies have begun to enjoy returns from the first fields to come into production; and there have been signs that new and cheaper technology for some of the more marginal fields may be introduced in a few years' time. In short, by late 1977 the British North Sea could reasonably be regarded as an established petroleum province which, although constituting a small proportion of world resources, might exercise an increasingly important role at the margin of world oil supplies (see Chapter 1).

In the rest of this chapter some of the technical, economic and political factors influencing the supply of North Sea oil are first explained. Then total supplies from the established commercial fields are reviewed. Next the large number of significant oil discoveries made by end-1976 is analysed and a range of fields likely to be exploited is selected. Finally, an ultimate North Sea production schedule is estimated, using a simple model to forecast the timing of developments from discoveries made in 1977 onwards.

NORTH SEA OIL RESERVE ESTIMATES

By mid-1977 the thousandth well had been drilled on the United Kingdom Continental Shelf. Fifteen North Sea oilfields had been declared 'commercial' and were either producing oil or were under development. Nearly forty other promising oil discoveries had been made in the North Sea, of which about half seemed likely to be exploited. In addition seven gas fields had been declared commercial and large deposits of gas associated with oil reserves had been proved. As Figure 3.1 shows, however, in 1976 additions to North Sea reserves were smaller than in the previous four years.

According to estimates explained in detail below, nearly 9000 million barrels of recoverable reserves appear to be contained in the fifteen

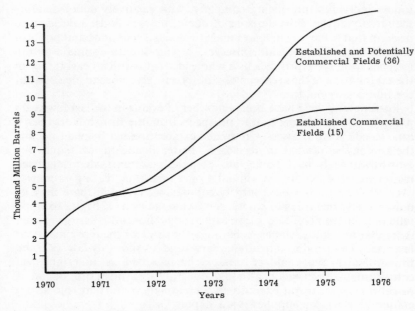

FIG 3.1　Recoverable Oil Reserve Estimates: UK North Sea

SOURCE Authors' estimates (at mid-1977, *not* at date of discovery).

established commercial fields and up to a further 5000 million in twenty-one other fields already found and likely to be developed. Current opinions as to the ultimate oil potential of the United Kingdom North Sea between 55° 50′ North and 62° North vary enormously but a reasonably likely range, assuming no significant change in the rate of recovery, is between 20,000 and 30,000 million barrels of recoverable reserves with a somewhat narrower consensus at 22–25,000 million barrels. It appears that up to two-thirds of the likely ultimate supplies of North Sea oil may already have been discovered; remaining reserves will probably come either from smaller prospects which are technically more complex to exploit or from deeper-water discoveries which may require technological innovation before they can be developed. Before reviewing these forecasts in detail, it may be useful to summarise some of the general technical problems in field reserve estimation.

A typical North Sea oil reservoir will be located at least 7000 feet below the sea-bed, have an area of several square miles and a gross thickness of the order of several hundred feet. A fundamental problem in reserve estimation is therefore the interpolation of reservoir characteristics between the small number – typically four to six – of exploration and appraisal wells drilled. The seismic information and associated geological and geophysical controls which are used to deduce reservoir geometries are now generally of a very high standard. In particular the new three-dimensional seismic techniques for well log interpolation apparently enable geologists to 'see' a reservoir below strata which had previously distorted the information gained by conventional techniques. Even so, in the first stage of assessing reserves by determining the volume of pore space in the reservoir sediments, a part of which may be occupied by oil, substantial errors or later revisions can occur. For example in the official estimates for 1977[2] the reserves of the Dunlin and Thistle fields were upgraded from the previous year's estimates by over 20 per cent, primarily as a result of seismic reinterpretation.

Other stages in the determination of technically recoverable reserves normally include the calculation of the net reservoir volume, the total volume of oil in place and a recovery factor. Net reservoir volumes are determined by subtracting the volume of impervious intervals within the reservoir from the gross volume. Lateral variations in the sediment properties, which are particularly common in North Sea reservoirs, may contribute to over-optimistic estimates of the total volume of oil in place, which is calculated from net reservoir volume by making various assumptions concerning the degree of water saturation within the pore space. A good example is the appraisal programme for the Brae field, where reservoir characteristics are irregular even over small areas because of the extremely variable nature of the sediments. When errors are accumulated at each stage in the oil-in-place calculation the total error margin may be at least ± 50 per cent.

SUPPLIES FROM ESTABLISHED COMMERCIAL FIELDS

The major proportion of oil supplies from the North Sea over the next ten years will come from oil fields already established as good commercial prospects. Table 3.1 compares the authors' estimates of reserves in the fifteen established commercial fields (compiled from a variety of oil industry and published sources) with the official 'Brown Book' figures for 1977. The estimates are generally very close, and, where significant differences arise, they are normally due to different definitions of reserves considered commercially recoverable. In some cases – Beryl, Piper and Thistle, for example – outlying reserves may eventually be brought into the established production system. But until substantial production experience has been gained all the estimates given in Table 3.1 must be regarded as tentative. So far at any rate, such experience has been largely favourable with individual wells on the Forties, Auk and Piper fields all flowing at rates initially in excess of

TABLE 3.1 Proved Recoverable Reserves Estimates: Established Commercial fields in UK Sector of the North Sea, 1977 (million barrels)

Field	Government estimate*	Authors' estimate
Argyll	na	30
Auk	60[a]	50
Beryl	520[b]	360
Brent	1700[ac]	1800
Claymore	420	450
Cormorant	150[a]	180
Dunlin	600[a]	590
Forties	1780	1750
Heather	150	200
Montrose	150	100
Murchison UK	na	300
Ninian	1040	1100
Piper	650	750
Statfjord UK	430	450
Thistle	560	540
Total	8540[d]	8650

[a] Total discounted reserves, that is proven plus suitably discounted figures for probable and possible reserves.
[b] Proved plus prospective.
[c] Black oil only, that is excluding condensate.
[d] Including authors' estimates for Argyll and Murchison UK.
na – Not available.
* SOURCE *Development of the Oil and Gas Resources of the United Kingdom,* (London: H.M. Stationery Office, for the Department of Energy, 1977)), the 'Brown Book'.

20,000 barrels per day. Less favourable results were experienced at Beryl, where the first production well yielded less than 2000 barrels per day, and at the small Argyll field, where the reservoir is believed not to have performed as well as had been anticipated and the life of the field may be less than initial expectations.

In Table 3.2 estimates are given of annual production from each of the established fields up to 1985. Whilst such forecasts should ideally be based on a rigorous technical and economic analysis of reservoir performance, useful, if rather crude, projections can be derived from a field's recoverable reserve figure and the design capacity of installed equipment. The former can be thought of as an ultimate cumulative production forecast of the amount of oil in the reservoir which can be recovered under established techniques and at the current cost:price ratio. The latter involves a compromise between the aims of achieving a

TABLE 3.2 Annual Production Estimates for Established Commercial Oilfields (thousand barrels per day)

Field	1975	1976	1977	1978	1979	1980	1981	1982	1983	1984	1985
Argyll	10	20	20	10							
Auk		20	40	40	21	9					
Beryl		10	70	90	90	90	90	82	70	59	50
Brent		2	40	140	270	370	440	450	450	365	325
Claymore			30	75	110	130	124	107	92	79	68
Cormorant					20	40	50	50	50	42	36
Dunlin					70	100	120	150	150	123	108
Forties	13	180	450	500	500	500	424	356	299	251	211
Heather				15	40	50	50	50	41	36	32
Montrose		2	25	45	50	26	21	18	15	12	10
Murchison UK						16	64	80	96	80	68
Ninian				110	200	290	320	320	231	201	175
Piper		5	120	250	250	229	192	161	136	114	96
Statfjord UK					5	10	25	45	55	65	70
Thistle			10	125	175	200	145	124	105	89	76
Total (million barrels per day)	0.02	0.2	0.8	1.4	1.8	2.1	2.1	2.0	1.8	1.5	1.3
(million tonnes per year)	1	12	40	69	88	100	101	97	87	74	64

SOURCE Authors' estimates.

high production level as soon as possible and of not jeopardising the production characteristics of the reservoir. With some over-simplification one can state the general aim as being to draw the oil out as fast as possible without allowing the underlying water to break through. As a rule, the higher the peak production figure and the longer production is sustained at this figure the more difficult it is to avoid a sudden sharp decline in reservoir productivity.

It is obviously impossible to know how individual operators will strike the balance just described: good oilfield practice is in reality just as hard to define as the national interest in a depletion control policy (see Chapter 2). The approach used here is therefore to take published estimates of peak production for each field and forecast rates of build-up to that peak from published information about development pro-grammes. Cumulative production up to the point of maximum pro-duction is then deducted from the recoverable reserve figure. By varying the number of years during which this peak figure is sustained and the percentage of residual reserves which may be recovered each year thereafter, a range of production profiles can be simulated. In practice several depletion percentages could be used for each profile but a simple exponential decline is employed in the calculations here. Finally, from the range of simulated production profiles one is selected which maximises the final recovery yet avoids an over-rapid production decline which would imply a technically sub-optimal rate of depletion. There is inevitably a large element of judgement in such calculations.

The output forecasts in Table 3.2 make no allowance for possible breaks in production because of accidents or other delays. Events such as the blow-out at the Ekofisk field in 1977 are a reminder of the increased possibility of accidents where new technology is being tried out or where established techniques are pushed to their limits. For example, a great deal of fundamental research has yet to be done on the long-term behaviour of large offshore concrete structures containing hot oil. The premature corrosion of riser pipes on Ekofisk and checks for similar effects on other North Sea production platforms emphasise the incomplete understanding of the long-term behaviour of such systems.

In general, although no great precision can be achieved, even within the limits of the surprise-free assumptions, in forecasting future oil supplies from the established commercial fields in the North Sea, the supply schedule for such fields is likely (for reasons given in subsequent chapters) to be much more robust with respect to changes in economic, technical and political factors than are the supply schedules for fields on which development has not yet begun and for assumed future disco-veries. Provided there are no serious accidents or other delays, there is a good chance that by the early 1980s the established commercial fields will be producing about 2 million barrels per day (100 million tonnes per year), as suggested in Figure 3.3.

SUPPLIES FROM POTENTIALLY COMMERCIAL DISCOVERIES

In the first few years of exploration in the North Sea, discoveries were made in a variety of geological settings. Once, however, the common characteristics of fields such as Brent, Dunlin and Thistle were established, success ratios in the most prospective area of the East Shetland basin improved enormously, particularly following the massive fourth round of licensing. At one time every second well yielded some large or small discovery of hydrocarbons. As Figure 3.1 indicates, however, more recently net additions to reserves have dropped, although the number of publicly announced 'significant' discoveries has been virtually unchanged. The average size of discoveries has tended to decline and indeed it seems probable that discoveries which during the boom period would not have been worth public confirmation beyond the non-committal announcement 'well plugged and abandoned' have recently been described as 'significant discovery requiring further appraisal'. This should be borne in mind when interpreting Table 3.3, which reproduces the official 'Brown Book' list of significant discoveries announced by end-1976 (excluding the established commercial fields).

TABLE 3.3 Significant* Oil Discoveries, 1973–76 (excluding Established Commercial Fields)

Field name	Block number	Discovered by	Date discovered
Maureen	16/29	Phillips Group	February 1973
–	3/15	Total Group	July 1973
Hutton	211/28	Conoco/BNOC/Gulf Group	September 1973
Alwyn	3/14a	Total Group	November 1973
Magnus	211/12	BP	June 1974
Andrew	16/28	BP	June 1974
–	9/13	Mobil Group	June 1974
Buchan	21/1	Transworld Group	August 1974
–	15/23	Texaco	October 1974
–	3/11	Amoco Group	December 1974
–	2/5	Union Oil Group	December 1974
–	15/16	Texaco	December 1974
–	14/20	Texaco	February 1975
–	9/12	Union Oil Group	February 1975
Crawford	9/28	Hamilton Group	February 1975
–	3/4	Texaco	March 1975
Tern	210/25	Shell/Esso Group	April 1975
–	2/10	Siebens Group	April 1975
Brae	16/7	Pan Ocean Group	April 1975
–	211/27	Amoco Group	April 1975

TABLE 3.3 (*contd.*)

Field name	Block number	Discovered by	Date discovered
Beryl North	9/13	Mobil Group	May 1975
–	21/2	Zapata Group	June 1975
–	3/2	Conoco/BNOC/Gulf Group	June 1975
–	211/13	Shell/Esso Group	July 1975
–	16/21	Sun Oil Group	August 1975
–	3/4	Texaco	August 1975
–	16/7	Pan Ocean Group	August 1975
Murchison	211/19	Conoco/BNOC/Gulf Group	September 1975
–	211/18	BODL Group	September 1975
–	15/13	BP Group	October 1975
–	3/9	Total Group	October 1975
–	15/21	Monsanto Group	October 1975
–	211/13	Shell/Esso Group	December 1975
–	23/27	Ranger/Scot Group	March 1976
–	23/26a	BP	March 1976
–	15/27	Phillips Group	April 1976
–	14/20	Texaco	April 1976
–	211/27	Amoco Group	May 1976
–	9/19	Conoco/BNOC/Gulf Group	May 1976
–	211/16	Shell/Esso Group	May 1976
–	14/20	Texaco	June 1976
–	3/7	Chevron/Canada Northwest Group	June 1976
–	16/17	Phillips Group	July 1976
–	211/18	BODL Group	July 1976
Beatrice	11/30	Mesa Group	September 1976

* The description 'significant' relates to the flow rates achieved in well tests, and this is not necessarily an indicator of the potential commercial value of the find.

SOURCE *Development of the Oil and Gas Resources of the United Kingdom* (London: H.M. Stationery Office, for the Department of Energy, 1977).

From Table 3.3 it can be seen that in 1975 a very large number of discoveries were made but there was a decline to twelve discoveries in 1976, which reflected a corresponding reduction in rig activity. The rate of discovery has in fact continued to be high relative to other areas of the world but only one of the 1976 finds seems likely to be developed (Beatrice) and with about 160–250 million barrels of recoverable reserves confirmed so far, it is certainly not a giant find like Brent or Statfjord.

Although the average size of discovery in the United Kingdom is declining as the exploration programme reaches maturity, a substantial backlog of potentially commercial discoveries apparently built up in the three-year period from 1974 to mid-1977 when no new production platform order was placed. The causes of this hiatus in the development programme are numerous: uncertainty about the future of world oil supplies and demand following the massive OPEC price increases in 1973–75; the world recession, in part precipitated by these increases; and (of specific importance to the companies engaged in the first round of oilfield development in the North Sea) the substantial uncertainties generated by changes in the fiscal system, by proposals for state participation and by the prospect of controls on rates of oilfield depletion. Some of these uncertainties are examined in detail in other chapters. With hindsight, one can also see now that the companies wanted to avoid a repetition of the rather disorderly scramble to achieve first oil production in the area, which brought about management problems for them and an excess demand for North Sea equipment and supplies. The companies are probably now convinced that the North Sea will be an important petroleum province for several decades. There is little fear of outright expropriation and most expectations are that the price of oil is unlikely to collapse. Therefore emphasis is now placed on developing a steady supply of oil from established projects in the North Sea so that the new projects can be funded from profits from established fields.

Given the substantial backlog of potentially commercial North Sea discoveries, it is naturally difficult to guess at an oil company's priorities for development. Indeed, there are several examples of fresh discoveries taking precedence over fields once thought to have a good chance of ultimate development. Table 3.4 gives some likely ranges of recoverable reserves for the twenty-one discoveries which are classified by the authors as potentially commercial: that is, discoveries which, on the assumptions of the surprise-free scenario, are likely ultimately to be developed.

Some of the fields listed in Table 3.4 have a much better chance of development than other, more marginal prospects. For example the Beatrice field discovered in September 1976 is a small to medium-sized accumulation in relatively shallow water only twelve miles from land. It is virtually certain to be developed, as are the Buchan and Tartan fields. At the other extreme the Hutton field lies in about 500 feet of water, has a complex structure and could probably not be easily exploited using conventional, fixed-platform, technology. In some cases (such as Magnus) appraisal drilling programmes have been completed and final confirmation of a development decision awaits design studies or government approval. In other cases (for example Brae and Thelma) the appraisal drilling programme has produced confusing results and recoverable reserve estimates have fluctuated sharply. Consequently, the reserve figures contained in Table 3.4 are subject to considerable error and should only be interpreted as a guide to supplies from known discoveries for which development plans have yet to be confirmed. Not

TABLE 3.4 (*a*) Recoverable Reserves Estimates for Potentially Commercial Oilfields

Field	Recoverable reserves (million barrels)	Estimated earliest production (start year)
Alwyn	200–300	1982
Alwyn Extension	100–200	1984
Andrew	150–200	1982
Beatrice	150–250	1980
Beryl Extension	100–200	1980
Brae	300–500	1982
Buchan	75–150	1979
Cormorant Extension	400–600	1982
Crawford	250–350	1982
Hutton	200–300	1983
Lyell	200–300	1982
Magnus	350–450	1981
Maureen + Mabel	75–150	1982
Tartan	250–350	1981
Tern	250–350	1983
Thelma	300–500	1982
3/4	100–200	1983
3/4–3/9	300–400	1983
9/12	100–200	1983
21/2	50–100	1982
211/27	200–300	1984
Total	4100–6350	

TABLE 3.4 (*b*) Aggregate Production Schedule for Potentially Commercial Oilfields (million barrels per day)

1981	1982	1983	1984	1985
0.1	0.4	0.9	1.3	1.5

SOURCE Authors' estimates.

all the fields may, in the event, be developed. It is the aggregate production schedule for potentially commercial fields, however, which is the prime concern here: this schedule is shown at the foot of Table 3.4.

SUPPLIES FROM FUTURE DISCOVERIES

As explained at the beginning of this chapter, estimates of the ultimate recoverable oil potential of the United Kingdom North Sea range between 20,000 and 30,000 million barrels, with a figure of 22–25,000 million barrels covering most official and industry estimates. These figures do not allow for what may be substantial additional reserves in areas north of the 62nd Parallel which have yet to be licensed and explored. There are also other United Kingdom offshore prospects such as the Celtic and Irish Seas, the Western Approaches (where the boundary with France was settled in 1977) and the so far disappointing areas west of the Shetland Islands.[3] A simple model is used here to generate a surprise-free projection of future North Sea oil discoveries in the area between 55° 50′ and 62° North. 'Future' finds are taken to be those made from 1977 onwards.

Some initial qualifications should be made. First, it is possible that future exploration and development schedules in the North Sea will differ radically from the established pattern. Much will depend on the oil industry's response to – and the role of the British National Oil Corporation (BNOC) in – future rounds of licensing, which like the fifth round are likely to be much smaller than the massive fourth round in 1971–72 when 282 blocks were allocated. The industry's response will in turn be a function of its global as well as its existing North Sea commitments. Moreover, the way in which the British Government's participation, tax and depletion policies work out in practice will have crucial effects on the exploration programme. It should also be pointed out that, although fields are classified in this chapter as 'established commercial', 'potentially commercial' or 'future discoveries', in practice the distinctions are not so definite. For example, in the future there may well be further development of outlying reserves close to established fields. In the Thistle field block, for instance, there are two structures close to the main field which could well be developed in conjunction with the existing production system and there are other outlying discoveries in the block which could conceivably be tied in as well. Similarly, the ranking of potentially commercial developments can change as new, more promising discoveries are made which are consequently given a higher priority. For example, it seems likely that development of Tern, which was at one time thought to be a highly promising medium-sized, deep-water field, will be pushed back because the shallower-water Fulmar field[4] with much lower capital costs appears to be a more attractive prospect.

In what follows, a surprise-free schedule of future developable discoveries is derived by making assumptions about the number of remaining prospective structures in the United Kingdom North Sea between 55° 50′ North and 62° North, the probabilities of locating fields of particular sizes and annual levels of drilling activity. The estimates assume the exploitation of small fields using new techniques which are not yet fully established but which can reasonably be included in a surprise-free projection. Inevitably, the modelling process for future finds is highly speculative but it is at least explicit. To repeat, it is intended as a surprise-free case for a particular offshore area — the United Kingdom North Sea between 55° 50′ and 62° North — which can be used as a standard against which to compare the effects, set out in later chapters, of alterations in key variables. Since the assumptions are explicit, those who disagree with them can readily substitute their own.

THE LEVEL OF DRILLING ACTIVITY

Table 3.5 records the number of mobile rig months spent in exploration and discovery appraisal during the period 1970 to 1976 in the East Shetlands, East Scotland and East England areas. Separate information on the time spent on exploration alone is not provided in the official statistics, although the number of exploration wells is known. During 1976, fifty-three exploration wells were drilled in these areas whereas seventy-four had been drilled the previous year. Using this information it appears that the average coefficient of *total* rig time (that is, exploration and appraisal) necessary to drill one exploration well in 1976 remained at approximately the same level as in 1975: about four and a half months.

If it is correct to assume that, as the exploration effort matures, a greater proportion of the wells drilled will be for appraisal, then it seems reasonable to expect that this ratio will increase (as it did in the early 1970s). In order to estimate the timing of future discoveries it is assumed that the ratio increases quite sharply until the end of 1978 (to six and a half months per well) when another round of licensing checks the increase. In 1981, however, the ratio begins to increase again sharply. By 1982 it is assumed to reach a plateau rate of nine months of mobile rig activity to one exploration well. It is assumed that the rate then remains constant to the end of the forecast period (see Table 3.8).

In line with the assumption that the exploration programme is maturing and that the most prospective structures have been drilled, it is likely that the *total* amount of rig time in the North Sea area will decrease. From a 1977 level therefore of 210 rig months it is assumed to halve by 1980 and to reach a plateau level of five rigs active per year, that is sixty rig months, in 1982. This is consistent with the view that United Kingdom North Sea exploration activity in the area between 55° 50′ and 62° North will decrease as interest heightens in areas to the north of the currently licensed areas (especially in Norwegian waters), to the west of the United Kingdom and in other offshore areas.

A summary of the forecast activity schedule is included in Table 3.8.

THE NUMBER OF STRUCTURES TO BE DRILLED

In estimating the number of prospective structures which have yet to be

TABLE 3.5 Mobile Rig Activity: Rig Time (in months) – Breakdown by Geographical Areas

Area	1970	1971	1972	1973	1974	1975	1976
East of Shetland	–	9.6	32.4	82.8	148.8	163.2	118.8
East of Scotland	26.4	38.4	49.2	45.6	98.8	144.0	100.8
East of England[a]	37.2	14.4	22.8	30.0	20.4	19.2	18.0
Total UK North Sea	63.6	62.4	104.4	158.4	268.0	326.4	237.6
Number of exploration wells	22	24	33	41	55	74	53
Coefficient (rig months per well)	2.9	2.6	3.2	3.9	4.9	4.4	4.5

[a] includes some exploration and appraisal time in southern (gas) basin.

SOURCE *Development of the Oil and Gas Resources of the United Kingdom* (London: H.M. Stationery Office, for the Department of Energy, 1977).

drilled in the United Kingdom North Sea between 55° 50′ and 62° North one of the few useful sources available is a study submitted to the Government early in 1975 by the United Kingdom Offshore Operators' Association (UKOOA),[5] although it necessarily reflects the economic, technical and political environment of the period when it was written. Some of the information from the UKOOA study is shown in Figure 3.2.

In the period 1970–74 the total number of exploration wells drilled in the East Scotland/East Shetlands areas was 137. For the same period the number drilled east of England was 38. Assuming half of the East of England wells were for gas exploration in the southern sector gives an oil exploration well total of 156. Using the UKOOA estimates of structures drilled (Figure 3.2), it appears that these 156 exploration wells tested 110 structures (135 less 25 drilled before 1970). Over this period, therefore, on average, 1.4 exploration wells were evidently necessary to test a structure.[6] Using this coefficient of 1.4, one can estimate that the 127 oil-exploration wells drilled in 1975 and 1976 (Table 3.5) would have tested about 90 structures – nearly 20 more than the UKOOA study forecast. The reason for this discrepancy appears to lie in the designation of wells. As more complex fields are appraised later in the exploration pro-gramme, geologists find it more difficult to define the limits of an accumulation and hence relatively more wells which are eventually found to have been investigating the same structure are designated as

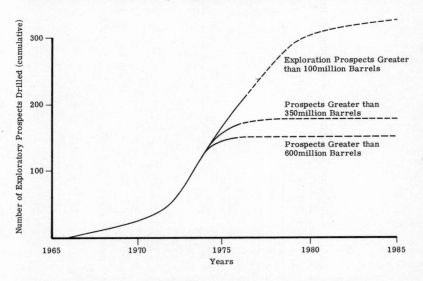

FIG 3.2   Oil Exploration in the UK North Sea, 55° 50′N to 62° 00′N

SOURCE Adapted from *A Report on the Proposed Petroleum Revenue Tax* (UK Offshore Operators' Association, 1975).

exploration wells. There may also be tax advantages in such a designation (see Chapter 5).

Although one must bear in mind the margin of error surrounding the coefficient of 1.4, it would appear that by the end of 1976 about 225 structures had been tested (110 + 90, plus 25 for the years prior to 1970). Since the UKOOA study put the total number of prospective structures in the United Kingdom North Sea between 55° 50′ and 62° North at around 300-350 (Figure 3.2), it can be estimated that at the end of 1976 some 75 to 125 structures remained to be drilled.

THE PROBABILITY OF LOCATING DEVELOPABLE DISCOVERIES

By end-1976 the exploration programme had confirmed about 14,000 million barrels of recoverable oil reserves in 36 established or potentially commercial fields (see Tables 3.1 and 3.4) from drilling approximately 225 structures. In order to model future finds using the historic probabilities of locating developable discoveries, these established discoveries are aggregated in Table 3.6 into size groups.

TABLE 3.6 Past Finds by Size of Field

Field size group (million barrels recoverable reserves)	Number of fields confirmed by end-1976	Probability of finding field of given size (number of fields in size group divided by total number of structures)
101–250	10	0.044
251–350	7	0.031
351–450	6	0.027
greater than 450	7	0.031
	30[a]	

[a] Six of the fields confirmed by end-1976 are estimated to have less than 101 million barrels of recoverable reserves and so are not included here.

SOURCES Authors' estimates and *Development of the Oil and Gas Resources of the United Kingdom* (London: H.M. Stationery Office, for the Department of Energy, 1977) the 'Brown Book'.

The probabilities given in Table 3.6 are a measure of the historic likelihood of making a developable discovery of given size. What is regarded as developable at any time depends, of course, on technical, economic and political circumstances and these will be different in the future. Moreover, the structures so far drilled include many of those which the companies believed to be the most promising. As Figure 3.2

suggests, by end-1975 UKOOA believed that only four prospects which could contain reserves greater than 600 million barrels remained and that these would all be tested in 1976. Similarly, by the end of 1976 nearly all those prospects greater than 350 million barrels were expected to have been explored. Thus the 100 or so remaining prospective structures to be drilled from 1977 onwards may well yield fields of smaller average size than discoveries made in the last few years.

It is obviously unreasonable to base fine distinctions on the limited information available, and in any case the objective of this chapter is to provide a surprise-free projection. So as a crude adjustment of the historic probabilities it is assumed that in future the probability of locating a field in the highest class (greater than 450 million barrels) is approximately halved and that the probability for the lowest class (101–250 million barrels) is doubled. The probability of finding a 250–350 million barrel field is left virtually unchanged and the probability of a 350–450 million barrel find is reduced by about one third. Table 3.7 shows the results.

TABLE 3.7 Assumed Probabilities of Future Discoveries

Field size group (million barrels recoverable reserves)	Probability of finding field of given size (historic)	(assumed future)	Implied number of developable finds for 100 remaining structures
101–250	.044	.090	9.0
251–350	.031	.030	3.0
351–450	.027	.020	2.0
greater than 450	.031	.015	1.5

SOURCE Table 3.6 and authors' estimates.

Table 3.8 brings together the results concerning future rig activity over the period to 1986 and the probabilities of locating developable prospects in the four size groups so as to show a time-profile of future discoveries. The profile is rounded to show whole field numbers since obviously one cannot discover fractions of fields.

A forecast for the remaining years up to 2000 is also included on the basis of a final reduction in annual exploration activity to average four rig years over the period 1987–2000. The probabilities of finding fields greater in size than 350 million barrels is taken to be insignificant by this time and hence no developable finds are entered for the two largest field size groups over this period.

TABLE 3.8 Future Rig Activity and Developable Fields

Year	Mobile rig activity (rig months) (A)	Coefficient[a] (B)	Exploration wells (C) (A ÷ B)	Structures tested (D) (C ÷ 1.4)	Prospective developable finds by field size (million barrels recoverable reserves) Number of finds				
					101–250 (D × .09)	251–350 (D × .03)	351–450 (D × .02)[b]	>450 (D × .015)[b]	Total
1977	210	5.5	38	27	2				2
1978	160	6.5	25	18	2	1			3
1979	120	7.0	17	12	1		1		2
1980	100	7.5	13	9	1	1		1	3
1981	80	8.5	9	6	1				1
1982	60	9.0	7	5					—
1983	60	9.0	7	5	1				1
1984	60	9.0	7	5		1			1
1985	60	9.0	7	5	1				1
1986	60	9.0	7	5			1		1
Sub-total				97	9	3	2	1	15
1987–2000	672	9.0	75	53	5	2	—	—	7
Total				150	14	5	2	1	22

a See p. 62.
b Zero for the period 1987–2000

SOURCE Tables 3.5 to 3.7 and authors' estimates.

By the end of the century the forecasts suggest that perhaps another twenty developable discoveries with reserves greater than 100 million barrels could be made. Of these about two-thirds would have less than 250 million barrels of recoverable reserves and probably only one or two would yield more than 450 million barrels. The total number of structures tested by the end of the century would be 375 – that is just above the UKOOA range. For comparison purposes Table 3.9 lists significant new oil finds for the year 1977 announced by the middle of the year. The table excludes wells which confirmed existing finds.

TABLE 3.9 Significant New Oil Finds in UK North Sea, Jan–July 1977

Block/Well	Operator	Remarks
211/19–6	Conoco	Separate find from Murchison. Oil flowed at good rates from a thin pay-zone in the Jurassic.
211/18–13	BNOC	Separate find from Thistle. Two miles north east of 211/18–12. Oil flowed at 9100 barrels per day.
16/17–4	Phillips	The Toni well encountered 500 feet of net pay. Good flow characteristics. Recoverable reserves tentatively estimated at 250–350 million barrels.
211/22–1	Sun	Successful oil well flowed at 1275 barrels per day.
30/16–7	Shell	An appraisal well on the Fulmar field discovered but not publicly announced as a new find in 1976.

SOURCE Press reports.

The schedule of future developable finds in Table 3.8 is clearly very sensitive to assumptions concerning future rig activity. During 1977 activity increased as operators tried to complete their drilling obligations under the large fourth round of licensing before handing back part of the licences in 1978. Future rounds of licensing will be important in determining rig activity and it is significant that the Government has announced its intention to have smaller but more regular allocations. The fifth round conducted in 1976–77 made available 71 blocks (of which only 34 were in the North Sea) for award at ministerial discretion – all with 51 per cent state participation through the British National Oil Corporation or the British Gas Corporation. These two organisations can also apply for licences at any time and the ability, particularly of the former, to develop an independent exploration team could significantly affect activity in the 1980s. Even so it is difficult to see how the momentum of exploration in the United Kingdom North Sea, which reached a record 113 wells (74 exploration, 39 appraisal) in 1975, can be sustained. In future licensing some balance will probably be struck between a highly selective approach as has been adopted in Norway, which may inhibit development decisions where fields extend into neighbouring unallocated blocks, and massive releases which could lead to shortages of equipment and supplies.

A NORTH SEA DEVELOPMENT SCHEDULE

It now remains to convert the discovery schedules constructed in earlier sections of this chapter into an aggregate estimate of supplies from established commercial fields, potentially commercial fields and future discoveries. But first the future discoveries in Table 3.8 have to be allocated to development schedules for a range of hypothetical field models which is appropriate for analysis in a later chapter. Here a difficulty arises, for each North Sea project is unique and in any case it is likely that models based solely on the established fields will be a poor guide to future experience. Furthermore, the UKOOA figures only include structures likely to yield reserves in excess of 100 million barrels. It is conceivable that, if technology improves further, fields with less than 100 million barrels will be developed perhaps employing reusable production systems: it seems reasonable to assume, on a surprise-free scenario, that such fields will be exploited.

Details of the construction of the hypothetical field models chosen are given in Chapter 4, but for present purposes it is sufficient to say that discoveries are allocated to five such models with recoverable reserves respectively of 100, 200, 300, 400 and 700 million barrels. The two smallest developments are assumed to employ novel production systems using tethered buoyant platforms with sub-sea well completions and tanker loading. The 300 and 400 million barrel models each have a single fixed steel platform with pipeline spur connections, and the 700 million barrel model has two platforms – one fixed and one tethered buoyant platform with sub-sea completions and satellite wells.

Since fields containing recoverable reserves of only 100 or 200 million barrels would generally be uneconomic to develop with present technology and at the present cost:price ratio, the development schedule for future discoveries is divided to identify separately supplies from the larger fields (300 million barrels and more). It is assumed that because of a more favourable cost:price ratio the development of all discoveries larger than 250 million barrels goes ahead as quickly as is technically possible and that the discovery dates indicated in Table 3.8 therefore mark the starting points of investment projects. For each size group indicated in the table, an average model field size is chosen as follows:

Field size range (million barrels)	Model field (million barrels)	Number of fields up to 2000*
251 – 350	300	5
351 – 450	400	2
greater than 450	700	1
		8 = 3 thousand million barrels

* From Table 3.8

If the 3 thousand million barrels of reserves recoverable from the 300, 400 and 700 million barrel fields are added to the established commercial and potentially commercial field estimates of 8.7 and about 5 thousand million barrels respectively (as given in Tables 3.1 and 3.4) it would appear that of the order of 5 to 8 billion barrels remain to be developed from individual discoveries containing less than 300 million barrels if the consensus ultimate reserve estimate given at the beginning of this chapter of 22–25,000 million barrels is to be achieved. The figures calculated in Table 3.8 suggest that about 2–3000 million barrels could come from the 14 fields in the 101–250 million barrel range assumed to be discovered. The remaining figure would have to be made up from developments with individual recoverable reserves of 100 million barrels or less and from structures not included in the UKOOA study.

It is obviously impossible to provide an accurate discovery or development forecast for small fields. But it seems likely that isolated fields – even those with access to reserves of 200–250 million barrels – will remain undeveloped until the early 1980s and that smaller fields will probably not be developed until well into the second half of the decade. For the size group in Table 3.8 of 101–250 million barrels it is assumed that the first 200 million barrel projects begin in 1981 (four years after discovery). The fourteen such fields are all assumed to be developed by the end of the century (Table 3.10). To provide some rough indication of possible supplies from structures not considered prospective in the UKOOA study it is assumed in Table 3.10 that the equivalent of one 100 million barrel field begins development each year between 1987 and 1992 with two a year thereafter. Although the simplifying assumption is made that all additions to reserves from such discoveries are in new fields, in practice additions to North Sea reserves might come from improved recovery from established commercial developments, re-evaluations of the recoverable reserves of such fields as new geological horizons are shown to be prospective, or as satellite field developments which do not require entirely separate production systems.

In Figure 3.3 the various surprise-free supply forecasts are brought together for the 15 established commercial fields, the 21 potentially commercial fields and the 44 assumed future discoveries. Supplies from future discoveries with reserves of less than 300 million barrels are

TABLE 3.10 Future Development from Discoveries with less than 250
Million Barrels Recoverable Reserves

	Number of fields discovered in range (101–250 million barrels)	Number of fields starting development	
		(200 million barrels)	(100 million barrels)
1977	2	–	
1978	2	–	
1979	1	–	
1980	1	–	
1981	1	2	
1982	–	2	
1983	1	3	
1984	–	1	
1985	1	1	
1986	–	–	
1987–2000	5	5	22
Total	14	14	22
Total recoverable reserves (thousand million barrels)		2.8	2.2

SOURCES Table 3.8 and authors' estimates.

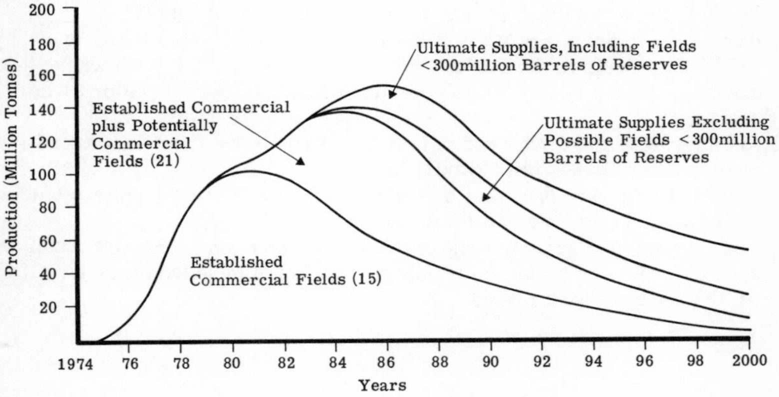

FIG 3.3 UK North Sea Oil Supplies (55°50′N to 62°00′N): Surprise-free
Projection

SOURCE Authors' estimates.

shown separately. The aggregate production schedule for the surprise-free projection shows UK North Sea oil supplies from the area between 55° 50′ and 62° North reaching about 150 million tons per annum by the mid-1980s. A relatively small volume of supplies is likely to be achieved from projects involving new technology (some 10–15 per cent of total production during the 1977–2000 period as a whole). Such sources could nevertheless become a significant part of total supplies in the 1990s as Figure 3.3 shows.

The surprise-free projection illustrated in Figure 3.3 is, of course, just one of the alternative possibilities in a rather uncertain supply outlook. It is easy to think of circumstances in which output might be substantially lower or higher than the top supply curve shown in the diagram. For instance, if one considers the whole United Kingdom offshore area, it is quite conceivable that reserves will be significantly greater than the highest figures suggested in this chapter. Unfortunately, at present there seems to be no basis for any reserve estimates for the non-North Sea offshore areas. In the chapters which follow, therefore, attention is still concentrated on the North Sea area between 55° 50′ and 62° North, but the sensitivity of supplies to changes in key variables is tested.

NOTES AND REFERENCES

1. An earlier version of some parts of this chapter appeared as Robinson and Morgan, *North Sea Oil and the British Economy* (London: Staniland Hall, 1977) pp. 5–20.
2. *Development of the Oil and Gas Resources of the United Kingdom* (London: H.M. Stationery Office, for the Department of Energy, 1977).
3. The first reasonably promising discovery west of Shetland was made by British Petroleum in the summer of 1977 but it is not clear whether the field can be exploited economically. See the *Financial Times*, London, 1 and 2 August 1977.
4. In block 30/16 and discovered in 1976 but not confirmed and announced as a commercial prospect until July 1977.
5. *A Report on the Proposed Petroleum Revenue Tax* (London: United Kingdom Offshore Operators' Association, 1975).
6. The coefficient is greater than one because, *inter alia*, there are technical problems with some wells and some structures not included in the UKOOA study may have been drilled.

CHAPTER 4

British North Sea Oilfields: Costs, Tax System and Rates of Return

In 1976 the North Sea accounted for more than 6 per cent of all fixed investment in the United Kingdom. According to estimates discussed in detail below, about £1500 million was spent on the construction and installation of production platforms, the manufacture of associated equipment, pipelines and terminals and on development drilling, compared with total Gross Domestic Fixed Capital Formation of about £23,000 million.[1] If all the potentially commercial fields described in Chapter 3 are eventually developed, investment could remain at or above these levels until the early 1980s. During that period the costs of operating the North Sea installations could rise to well over £500 million per annum. Such investments in one industry probably have no precedent in modern times in this country — perhaps only the great rail construction boom of the last century can provide a similar example of such large-scale enterprise. Then, however, the necessary finance was raised in this country: now well over half the money has come from abroad.

This chapter examines in detail the costs and likely post-tax company returns from investment in the United Kingdom North Sea. Since each project is unique the estimates are considered field by field. A range of cost models which will be used to simulate future North Sea developments is also introduced. Here the warning must be repeated that in the North Sea the past is at best only a rough guide to likely future trends, for it applies equally to costs as to oil supplies. One has only to look at the changes in North Sea exploitation costs in the recent past to realise how difficult it is to make long-term assessments of cost movements. Nevertheless, cost forecasts are basic to any analysis of the future of the British North Sea area and of government policy so they must be made. The reader should bear in mind that the intention in making forecasts of costs and of all cost-dependent variables (such as company profitability and government revenues) is simply to attempt a very broad assessment of future trends.[2] The error margins are bound to be wide but there is no precise way of quantifying them.

INVESTMENT COSTS

THE ESTABLISHED COMMERCIAL FIELDS

During the period 1973–75 when world oil prices were soaring, the costs of developing North Sea oil also increased far beyond the worst expectations of the operators. Most of the dozen or so fields involved in this first round of investment required enormous expenditures before any oil could be produced: investment in the Forties field for example began in 1971 and by the time production commenced in 1975 about 80 per cent of the total capital costs had been committed. Over this period projections of the eventual out-turn cost more than doubled and at one time it was taken as a working principle that the remaining costs would always be the same as the original estimate for developing the whole field.

It is not proposed to examine here in detail the causes of North Sea cost escalation in the early 1970s, which included a poor initial understanding of the engineering problems involved, a telescoping of the exploration, design and development programmes and competition for short supplies. A government study found that a shortage of elementary information on the North Sea environment was often the single most important item in raising costs since the consequent design amendments had to be made whilst construction was actually in progress. This suggests that operators misjudged the novel risks involved and were wrong in believing that North Sea projects would differ only in scale from other offshore projects around the world. To quote the study:

> It is fully recognised that in the absence of any records of comparable previous projects, project estimators were ill-equipped to calculate costs except by personal judgement and interpretation of previous experience. It is, nonetheless, surprising that the collective assessment was so poor and that no glowing exceptions appear. [3]

As a guide to the allocation of capital costs between the major items of expenditure, Table 4.1 provides a capital development cost schedule for a hypothetical 400 million barrel single-platform field discovered in 1977. The figures are derived mainly from discussion with oil companies involved in the development of new North Sea fields. The schedule assumes a delay between discovery and platform ordering of two to three years and a trouble-free construction period enabling the platform to be installed five years after discovery, with production beginning the following year. The development drilling period is taken to be four to five years.

The total undiscounted investment necessary to develop the 400

TABLE 4.1 Development Schedule for a 400 Million–barrel Field Discovered 1977

Year	Event	Investment (£ million)[a]
1	Discovery	4
2	Appraisal	9
3	Appraisal/Platform order	43
4	Construction	55
5	Construction	115
6	Tow-out	133
7	Development Drilling/Production start	56
8–11	Development Drilling continues	111
Total		526

Note expenditures include: exploration and appraisal drilling, platform construction and installation, platform facilities, loading buoy and lines, development drilling.

[a] Expressed in current prices.

SOURCE Authors' estimates.

million barrel field is put at £526 million (in current prices, not real terms) — equivalent to £1.3 per barrel of recoverable reserves or $2.2 per barrel at $1.70 to £1.00. An alternative index, widely used in the oil industry, is the investment required to achieve a barrel of peak daily production. Assuming a peak production rate of 100,000 barrels per day, each barrel of peak daily production would cost £5260. This is about ten times the initial estimates given for fields of comparable size in the first round of developments. Disaggregation of the cost schedule according to major items of expenditure suggests that the basic platform jacket would account for about a quarter of total costs, with platform equipment a similar proportion. Installation of the platform alone may take up to 10 per cent of all costs. It is also worth noting the relatively small amounts spent on exploration and appraisal, emphasising that although each well drilled may cost £5 million or more the additional information gained on likely reservoir size and performance may amply justify the expense involved.

The wide disparity in unit capital costs among fields is shown in Table 4.2, which gives estimated costs[4] for the fifteen established commercial fields (see Chapter 3, Table 3.1). Undiscounted capital costs vary from 40 pence per barrel for the prolific Piper field to over £1.80 for the small Montrose field. Although these two extremes correspond with the size difference between the two fields there is no clear indication of economies of scale, because there are many variables other than the size of reserves which influence costs (for example, depth of water, distance

TABLE 4.2 Capital Cost Estimates: Established Commercial and Potentially Commercial Fields (£ Million)

(15) Established commercial fields	1971	'72	'73	'74	'75	'76	'77	'78	'79	'80	'81–'85	Total to 1985	Unit Cost (£/barrel produced)[a]
Argyll		2	8	14	7	0	0	0	0	0	0	31	1.4
Auk	2	5	6	11	17	9	8	4	0	0	0	62	1.3
Beryl			5	34	69	86	50	22	12	0	0	278	0.8
Brent	5	10	21	28	138	301	400	385	238	102	146	1774	0.9
Claymore					31	129	75	38	6	0	0	279	0.6
Cormorant				2	10	31	75	62	53	20	17	270	1.7
Dunlin			3	8	52	86	65	38	36	38	84	410	0.7
Forties	14	40	91	140	173	107	75	33	24	13	0	710	0.4
Heather				3	14	52	90	49	24	13	0	245	1.4
Montrose		2	5	17	52	43	20	11	0	0	0	150	1.8
Murchison UK					4	26	65	148	154	32	22	451	1.7
Ninian			5	17	111	365	400	220	119	76	96	1409	1.4
Piper		2	5	42	104	64	40	22	12	0	0	291	0.4
Statfjord UK				3	3	34	40	60	53	32	34	259	0.7
Thistle		2	13	34	87	120	140	44	24	13	0	477	0.9
Sub-total	21	63	162	353	872	1453	1543	1136	755	339	399	7096	0.8
(21) Potentially commercial fields	0	2	3	3	21	94	154	392	680	1201	5140	7690	1.6
Grand Total	21	65	165	356	893	1547	1697	1528	1435	1540	5539	14786	1.1

[a] Undiscounted total costs divided by the total production to the end of the field's life or to 2000, whichever is earlier.

SOURCE Authors' estimates.

from shore, producing characteristics of the reservoir). For instance, the Ninian field with about 1100 million barrels of recoverable reserves has a unit capital cost of £1.4, yet the Claymore field with less than half the reserves of Ninian is estimated to have a unit cost of only £0.6 per barrel. Finally, attention should be drawn to the dominant effect of the giant fields on the cost schedule: three fields — Brent, Ninian and Forties — alone account for over half the investment in the proved fields.

THE POTENTIALLY COMMERCIAL FIELDS

Also included in Table 4.2 is an aggregate capital cost schedule for the twenty-one potentially commercial fields — discoveries which seem likely ultimately to be developed (see Chapter 3, Table 3.4). The information on which these costs are based is, of course, very much more speculative than for the established commercial fields. Consider for example the case of just one of the probable developments — the Buchan field, which lies in blocks 21/1 and 20/5. It was discovered in August 1974 and, despite some difficulty in testing, good flow rates from three intervals were announced. Some early reports suggested that the field might contain 600 million barrels of recoverable reserves. The first appraisal well was also successful: it tested five intervals, some of which may have been in a new productive geological sequence (the Devonian). Recoverable reserve estimates then rose to over 700 million barrels and the field was given a name. The three subsequent appraisal wells were, however, disappointing, and the geology of the field turned out to be much more complex than had been thought at first. Reserve estimates dropped dramatically and the initial development plans to use a fixed steel platform and pipeline transportation were dropped. In May 1977 British Petroleum (BP) acquired a majority stake in the field and plans for further appraisal were announced. Although by this time reserve estimates had dropped to 75–150 million barrels, it was eventually announced that the field could still be developed using a converted semi-submersible rig and sub-sea well completions.

Although Buchan is a well-publicised example of how initial development cost estimates are highly sensitive to the results of subsequent field appraisal it is certainly not atypical. Brae, Thelma, Hutton, Maureen, Tern and Alwyn, amongst other probable developments, have all given rise to initial euphoria on discovery followed by subsequent disappointment on appraisal. Then, as geological understanding has improved, the most pessimistic reserve estimates have also been discounted and as confidence has returned a more modest development programme has been announced. The psychological effect of naming a 'field' in this process cannot be too strongly emphasised: industry commentators invariably give such an event substantial press coverage although the commercial decision actually to develop the field may be months or even years hence. Conversely, promising unnamed prospects such as those in blocks where fields are already established often pass unnoticed.

The aggregate cost schedule for the probable fields given in Table 4.2 is derived from field-by-field estimates using the hypothetical field models, described in the next section, as a guide in addition to published information and oil industry sources. In all cases where recoverable reserves of 300 million barrels or more are indicated, a fixed-platform model is employed (see Chapter 3). Some of these fields may, of course, eventually employ novel technology but the cost models based on conventional techniques are a useful benchmark against which innovations can be assessed. According to Table 4.2, the capital costs of the twenty-one potentially commercial fields could over the period to 1985 be at least equal to the total capital costs of the fifteen proved fields, although the former are of much smaller average size (about 250 million barrels against 600 million barrels recoverable reserves).

CAPITAL COSTS OF DEVELOPING FUTURE FINDS

In Chapter 3, as part of a surprise-free supply projection, an attempt was made to simulate future oil supplies from discoveries made in the period 1977–2000. Each assumed find was allocated to one of five hypothetical field models with recoverable reserves respectively of 100, 200, 300, 400 and 700 million barrels. Since without new production technology it is unlikely that any prospect with less than 300 million barrels will be developed, in estimating the possible capital costs of future supplies of North Sea oil account must be taken of technical innovations which could ultimately lead to lower costs. Development schedules for the hypothetical fields are summarised in Table 4.3 and the models are described individually below.

The 300 and 400 million barrel fields in Table 4.3 are each single-platform projects in which oil is transported to shore using a tanker loading system. It is assumed that the water depth is 450 feet and the reservoir lies at 7000 feet below the sea-bed. The maximum achieved well productivity is 7000 barrels per day and the wells are established at a rate of six per year in the ratio of eight oil wells to six water injection wells to one gas-injection well. The cost figures given are highly sensitive to the depth of water, the depth to the reservoir and the distribution of reserves. The models are therefore for fields in which access to the full reserve potential is from a single platform without resort to outlying sub-sea completions. To the extent that such sub-sea techniques have to be used to achieve equivalent recoveries from awkwardly distributed reserves, costs will be correspondingly increased. Similarly, the cost schedule is highly sensitive to the timing of the various events identified in Table 4.1, particularly if the rates of price escalation applied to the costs turn out to be different from expectations. Furthermore, although

TABLE 4.3 Model Field Specifications[a]

	1977	'78	'79	'80	'81	'82	'83	'84	'85	'86	'87	'88	'89	'90	'91	'92	'93	'94	'95	'96	'97	'98	'99	2000	Total[c]
Production (thousand barrels per day)																									(million barrels)
200	0	0	0	45[b]	60	60	60	52	43	36	31	26	22	18	15	13	11	9	8	6	5	0	0	0	190
300	0	0	0	0	0	0	20[b]	50	80	80	80	67	58	50	44	38	33	29	25	22	19	17	14	13	269
400	0	0	0	0	0	0	10[b]	45	75	100	100	84	75	67	59	53	47	42	37	33	30	26	23	21	339
700	0	0	0	0	0	0	45[b]	70	105	135	150	150	150	150	130	112	97	84	73	63	54	47	41	35	618
Operating costs (£ million)																									(£ million)
200	0	0	0	17	23	24	25	25	25	25	25	25	25	25	25	25	25	25	25	25	25	0	0	0	446
300	0	0	0	0	0	0	13	26	27	29	29	29	29	29	29	29	29	29	29	29	29	29	29	29	496
400	0	0	0	0	0	0	16	33	34	36	36	36	36	36	36	36	36	36	36	36	36	36	36	36	619
700	0	0	0	0	0	0	19	43	62	71	71	71	71	71	71	71	71	71	71	71	71	71	71	71	1197
Capital costs (£ million)																									(£ million)
200	57	100	64	18	7																				246
300	4	9	39	48	98	124	54	26	20	14	15														453
400	4	9	43	55	114	133	56	26	27	29	29														524
700	4	9	115	175	194	153	56	26	124	193	132	28													1209

[a] Field sizes (200, 300, 400, 700) are expressed in million barrels of recoverable reserves.
[b] First year of production: 200 and 700 fields, 9 months; 300 and 400 fields, 6 months; with corresponding reduction in operating costs.
[c] Individual years' values are rounded and so may not add up to total.
SOURCE Authors' estimates, which for the 200 Field were greatly assisted by discussions with Vickers Offshore Development.

the installation of North Sea platforms is now less weather-sensitive, a delay of a few weeks during the critical period before the onset of winter can lead to an irreplaceable loss of valuable installation time.

As the cost of fixed-platform structures increases with the second or third power of the water depth, at depths greater than about 600 feet such installations become too expensive for the North Sea. This has created a powerful incentive to develop new techniques appropriate for the North Sea environment where development costs are less depth-dependent, an obvious solution being to place some or all of the production equipment on the sea-bed. An added incentive is that many of the fields in the North Sea for which an investment decision has yet to be taken have awkwardly distributed reserves and could not be adequately drained from a conventional fixed platform. Hence sea-bed completions, irrespective of water depth, could improve recovery factors.

There are, however, still serious, even fundamental, problems with the technology of sub-sea production.[5] For example, the pipe or riser connecting a group of sub-sea wellheads to a floating or semi-submersible treatment and shipment system, such as a converted drilling rig, must be able to accommodate enormous stresses. Second, although the idea of encapsulating the sea floor wellhead with a 'dry' chamber at atmospheric pressure, allowing easier access for maintenance, is attractive, the possibility of highly inflammable gas leakages is so serious as to have discouraged several potential manufacturers. Instead they have developed either completely 'wet' diver or remotely-serviced systems or, in one case, a system in which water at atmospheric pressure occupies the wellhead chamber. This last system appears to offer an attractive compromise between safety considerations and ease of access for maintenance. Which of the three, if any, is eventually adopted on a wide scale in the North Sea has yet to be determined. Indeed it is likely that all will at least be tried, even if only as temporary production systems.

Sub-sea production systems could be used in a number of ways — for example, to achieve and test early production on a field before a fixed platform is installed, or in conjunction with tethered buoyant platforms of various designs with or without associated storage systems to develop complete fields, or as satellite wells to tie in neighbouring reservoirs or outlying reserves in an established field to existing production equipment on fixed platforms. All these uses may eventually emerge although, until the performance of limited sub-sea completions already tied into fixed platforms at the Brent, Thistle and Beryl fields can be accurately assessed, wide-scale adoption is unlikely. There are also important problems to be overcome in the design of floating production platforms: deck loads for example are much more restricted than on fixed platforms and so equipment manufacturers will have to develop lighter facilities. The difficulty of designing tethered platform anchoring systems suitable for the North Sea environment is another important barrier to their introduction.

Although the acceptability of sub-sea production systems is of great technical interest (not least because of their ultimate worldwide usage in deep water), as explained in Chapter 3 the likely supplies from such systems in the United Kingdom North Sea between 55° 50′ and 62° North are likely to be modest in comparison to supplies from conventional developments in the foreseeable future. Therefore, relatively simple cost models are used for the 100 and 200 million barrel hypothetical fields. Table 4.3 shows the assumptions used for the 200 million barrel field, which is the smallest field model used in subsequent chapters.

The remaining hypothetical model – for a field with 700 million barrels of recoverable reserves – is derived using a combination of the 400, 200 and 100 million barrel models as follows. It is assumed that the field's development begins in 1978 with the main fixed-platform project one year after discovery. Production starts six years later (in 1984) from this platform via a short spur line to a trunk pipeline. Two outlying reservoirs are also produced, however, the larger one (with 200 million barrels reserves) beginning production via tanker loading a year earlier, and the other (with 100 million barrels reserves) five years later as production begins to decline from the main platform. A short pipeline spur connects the smaller reservoir to the main platform.

NORTH SEA OPERATING COSTS

The major part of expenses incurred in the first few years in developing a North Sea oilfield will be on capital items such as production platforms, associated equipment, pipelines and terminals. So heavily 'front-end-loaded' is the investment that even though substantial sums have been committed for nearly a decade to North Sea projects very few oil companies have yet been able accurately to quantify their likely North Sea operating costs: early estimates tended to be simple extrapolations of experience in areas such as the much less severe environment of the Gulf of Mexico. Operating costs have, in discounted terms, a much smaller influence on the returns from most projects, although in absolute terms they may equal or even exceed the initial investment.

It would be wrong to give the impression, as do many published estimates, that capital expenditure ceases once a field goes into production. At the margin it is difficult to determine whether an item of expenditure is necessary to enhance a field's performance or prevent a decline (and is therefore a capital item) or whether it is merely sustaining its present level (and is therefore an operating cost). Most North Sea fields will continue to incur both capital and operating expenditures throughout the field's life. Indeed, concern is sometimes expressed in the oil industry that a formidable item of expenditure may be incurred at the end of a project's life if platforms have to be removed. Despite the difficulty of drawing any precise line between capital and operating costs, the distinction is retained for the sake of convenience in this chapter.

Operating costs for North Sea oilfields can be divided into several broad categories:

(i) platform operating costs, including supplies, well servicing, labour and transport;

(ii) the costs of transporting the oil either by pipeline or by tanker to shore;

(iii) insurance costs for the platform, transportation and shore installations;

(iv) the cost of directly related onshore operations such as a treatment and transhipment terminal; and

(v) administrative expenses.

Within each category there will be considerable variation between fields. As with capital costs there is no clear correlation between unit operating costs and field size, but to some extent a high unit operating cost may follow a policy of avoiding heavy initial capital expenditure. This is especially the case for the method of shipment adopted in that, to achieve the same production, pipelines require more investment than tanker loading but they usually offer lower unit operating costs if employed at or near full capacity. Even where spare capacity exists, this may offer an attractive return if sold to the operators of neighbouring fields wishing to use the line.

Early estimates of North Sea operating costs, based on Gulf of Mexico experience, were of the order of 50 cents per barrel. Since then forecasts have not only been drastically revised upwards but some operators have declared that most of their operating costs will be fixed. Rules of thumb relating operating costs to capital investment have occasionally been used, but the most common argument for virtually fixed operating costs is that a field will handle roughly the same total volume of fluids each year in its life – mainly oil, with relatively modest water reinjection in the early years and vice versa as production declines.

On the other hand some operators continue to advocate use of an operating cost which is partly related to production. This is because they consider that unbroken production will very rarely be achieved, because of accidents, mechanical failures, market conditions or political intervention, and in consequence it may be more appropriate to allocate costs to physical production rather than to arbitrary time-periods. The relative importance of the various operating cost items may also change from time to time. Until a platform is installed and development drilling is completed, for example, it is likely that insurance charges could make up as much as a third of all operating costs. In later years such charges could be absorbed in the company's global policies at much more modest rates, or the company may choose not to insure the installations on the market but to bear the risks itself. Equally hard to quantify is the likely impact of any learning curve effect on operating costs – new equipment is bound to have teething problems and even when no such problems arise it is likely that a more experienced labour force will achieve lower-cost operations.

The following procedure is used to calculate the operating costs given in Table 4.4. After discussions with a number of oil companies an estimate of the likely total costs of operating each field at its plateau production rate is first made in 1977 prices. These costs expressed in 1977 terms are then transformed into current prices by increasing them

TABLE 4.4 Operating Cost Estimates: Established Commercial and Potentially Commercial Fields

(15) *Established commercial fields*	*Operating cost (£ per barrel production[a])*	*Typical annual operating cost (£ million)*
Argyll	2.2	15
Auk	1.2	13
Beryl	1.7	31
Brent	1.6	123
Claymore	1.3	27
Cormorant	1.2	14
Dunlin	1.4	35
Forties	1.0	84
Heather	1.7	18
Montrose	2.4	21
Murchison UK	2.0	32
Ninian	1.5	71
Piper	0.8	27
Statfjord UK	0.7	13
Thistle	1.8	45

Aggregate operating cost schedule: established commercial (15) and potentially commercial (21) fields
(£ million)

1975	1976	1977	1978	1979	1980	1981	1982	1983	1984	1985	Total
26	110	254	382	472	553	615	739	865	941	968	5925

[a] Undiscounted total costs divided by total production to the end of the field's life or to 2000, whichever is earlier.

SOURCE Authors' estimates.

at approximately half the forecast annual rates of increase of the index of wholesale prices of manufactured products (home sales) – see note 4. This escalation procedure is used until three or four years after production begins, by which time the field will be at its plateau rate of output. Where production begins part-way through a year or a multi-platform project is involved, appropriate adjustments are made to the rate of build-up of operating costs. Once, however, the field's plateau level of output is reached, total operating costs (*not* unit costs) are held constant in money terms, implying that declining insurance charges and the learning curve effect will tend to offset further inflationary pressures. As production declines *unit* operating costs will, of course, tend to increase since total costs are held constant. A similar procedure is used for the hypothetical fields' estimated operating costs which are given in Table 4.3.

As with the capital cost schedules, there are large differences in unit operating costs: the pipeline-connected fields, such as Piper and Forties, generally but by no means invariably have lower costs than the tanker-loading operations such as Argyll and Montrose. Some of the fields have unit operating costs in some years of more than £5 per barrel. Although such costs, when added to capital costs, may appear very high in relation to likely prices, one has to be cautious in drawing conclusions about the interrelationship between field costs, prices and supply behaviour. This issue is analysed in terms of avoidable and unavoidable costs in Chapter 6.

TAXATION OF BRITISH NORTH SEA OIL

By 1980 government revenue from the taxation of North Sea oil including receipts from royalties, Petroleum Revenue Tax and Corporation Tax could be running at £2–4000 million a year (see Chapter 9). The 'take' from individual fields will vary but will probably be of the order of 70 per cent of net company revenues (gross revenues less all costs). For the Brent field, for example, with per barrel undiscounted unit capital and operating costs estimated at £0.9 and £1.6 respectively the average government take could be approximately £9 per barrel of production (under the Use of Monopoly Power price scenario – see Chapter 6 for a detailed description). Whilst Brent is likely to be a relatively profitable field, even much less attractive prospects should still yield of the order of £6 per barrel in government revenue.

The various elements of the tax and royalty system for United Kingdom North Sea oil production are outlined below and in Chapter 5 a further review is given.[6] Chapter 5 also includes a detailed comparison of the British system with that operating in Norway, which is the only other European country likely to be self-sufficient in oil in the foreseeable future.

The Government's share of North Sea revenues, setting aside any amounts it may receive by way of state participation or profit remittances from the British National Oil Corporation, consists of three parts: royalties, Petroleum Revenue Tax and Corporation Tax. There are also licence rental fees which may be deducted from royalties and taxes (under production licences granted in the first four rounds) but since they make up a very small fraction of total projected government revenue they are not considered further. In certain circumstances capital gains tax may also apply to the disposal of North Sea assets but again this is likely to be relatively insignificant.

Royalties are calculated at the rate of 12.5 per cent of the wellhead value of the oil for licences granted in the first four rounds, or at the same percentage of the tax reference price of oil under the fifth (1977) licence round. The wellhead value is calculated by deducting the cost of transporting the oil to land from its landed market value. The assessment of an allowable transportation charge leaves scope for considerable argument (for instance about appropriate rates of return) and it is believed that disputes have continued for many years over such deductions for the southern basin gas fields. Even the apparent simplification introduced in the fifth licensing round of making royalties payable on the tax reference price has not solved the problem altogether. For it has yet to be stated clearly how such prices are to be defined in the great majority of cases where intra-group transfers take place rather than there being open-market sales. But since the North Sea producers are likely to be price-takers in the world oil market (see Chapter 1), it is assumed that world oil prices, suitably adjusted for freight and quality differentials, will be the basis for royalty and all other tax assessments. Royalties are here calculated by first making an estimated transportation charge adjustment (where necessary) to the nominal rate of 12.5 per cent, which is then multiplied by the gross sales revenues to yield the actual royalty payable.

Petroleum Revenue Tax (PRT) is a new tax introduced in the Oil Taxation Act (1975) and levied at a rate of 45 per cent on specially defined profits from offshore operations. Its introduction was prompted by claims that the oil companies would make excessive profits on their North Sea assets as a result of the massive oil price increases in the 1973–75 period. It was also claimed that, as things stood, the very large tax-allowable losses which the companies had accumulated under the posted price system could have seriously reduced any otherwise taxable North Sea profits. Most politicians were therefore agreed on the need to ensure that a greater share of the benefits from the North Sea accrued in the form of tax revenues. As introduced to Parliament, PRT had some of the features of a barrelage tax, in that it was to be levied on the production revenues from each field every six months, and some of the features of a conventional income tax in that various costs were to be allowed in computing the tax assessable profit including an additional 'uplift' on approved capital expenditures.

The proposals caused some alarm in the oil industry, which emphasised the sharp rise in the costs of North Sea projects. Many amendments were made to the original proposals yet the Government, anxious not to reduce potential revenue, stuck to a field-by-field basis of assessment. Instead of allowing the more profitable fields to 'subsidise' the so-called marginal prospects, various concessions were introduced which were designed to reduce the tax burden on projects with high unit costs. These concessions were introduced in some haste and, as is shown in Chapter 5, they may not always have the effects originally intended. There are two particularly important concessions: the production allowance, under which the revenue equivalent of 10 million long tons of oil is exempted from the tax when claimed at no more than half a million tons in any six-monthly tax period; and the annual limit on tax payable. This latter concession ensures that in any year the total PRT payable will not exceed 80 per cent of the amount by which an adjusted profit figure is greater than 30 per cent of the accumulated capital expenditure of the project. The adjusted profit can be defined approximately as the gross sales revenue for the year, less royalties and operating costs. The 'annual limit clause' typically has the effect of tapering a field's PRT charge and eventually eliminating it earlier than would have occurred without the concession. But it also places an upper limit on the tax payable by the most profitable fields.

Corporation Tax on North Sea profits is essentially the same as for any other industry, with the important restrictions contained in the Oil Taxation Act which place a so-called 'ring fence' round a company's North Sea operations. The purpose of this device is to ensure that corporate tax liability on profits from United Kingdom oil production is not reduced by relief for losses and other allowances incurred in other areas of a company's business. In practice, it isolates a company's United Kingdom oil extraction activities for Corporation Tax (and for an individual's income tax) purposes. Thus whereas for Petroleum Revenue Tax the unit of assessment is the individual field, for Corporation Tax the unit may include one field or several, each of which may involve investment expenditures in different years.

It can be seen, therefore, that a rather different tax schedule will result when a company is involved in multi-field investments (see Chapter 5) from that when, as assumed in this chapter, the tax is calculated on a field-by-field basis. Corporation Tax is calculated after deducting licence royalties, operating costs, miscellaneous charges including any loan interest, capital allowances and PRT from gross trading revenue. There is no 'uplift' available for expenditure otherwise allowable against corporation taxable profits, but 100 per cent immediate allowances are assumed.

PROFITABILITY OF NORTH SEA OIL

Having assessed the likely magnitudes of North Sea oil supplies, capital and operating costs and the structure of the tax system it is now possible to draw some preliminary conclusions about likely profitability, using the output, cost and tax assumptions already explained. Further comments on profitability appear in later chapters. Chapter 5 discusses how variations in tax rates may affect profitability, in Chapter 6 the effect of alternative price forecasts is considered, and in Chapter 7 the impact on returns of government depletion control is assessed. Chapter 9 reviews the likely size of aggregate government revenues from United Kingdom North Sea oil developments. The returns quoted in this chapter assume that the relevant tax rates and the tax system remain as at present.

Previous sections of this and earlier chapters have stressed the ignorance which persists concerning production and cost figures, even for established fields. If anything, oil prices are even more unpredictable, so a range of forecasts or scenarios is used in Chapter 6 to estimate the sensitivity of profitability to price variations. Here, however, only one scenario is used, since the aim is merely to establish a benchmark comparison of the range of returns. Accordingly, the 'crude price indexation' (CPI) scenario is taken in which, briefly, North Sea oil prices are assumed to increase from their mid-1977 level of about $14.5 per barrel at a compound rate of 5 per cent per annum from 1977 to 1985 and at 7 per cent per annum from 1985 to 1995. The resultant after-tax returns for the fifteen proved fields and a selection of the potentially commercial fields, calculated from a series of computer programs which incorporate the United Kingdom tax system for offshore oil, are given in Table 4.5. Abortive exploration expenditures are excluded but exploration which can be attributed to particular fields is included. There may well be other costs which could be attributed to the fields by the companies concerned but for which no information is available: the returns shown here are only on development expenditures and are therefore not true indicators of corporate returns.

As tends to happen with published figures on North Sea project returns, it is easy to ascribe to the estimates given in Table 4.5 an accuracy that is out of all proportion to the quality of information on which they are based. The use of computers for such calculations does, of course, greatly accelerate the preparation of such figures and they are therefore invaluable for investigating the consequences of changes in assumptions. But it must be emphasised that the returns quoted in Table

4.5 are only intended to give an approximate idea of the profitability of North Sea fields on the basis of certain assumptions about production, costs, taxes and oil prices many years into the future. They can perhaps best be regarded as a quantification of present company expectations rather than as a forecast of the likely profitability outcome.

TABLE 4.5 Estimated Profitability of North Sea Oilfields after Tax
Crude Price Indexation Scenario[a]

Commercial fields	IRR % current prices	IRR % real terms	NPV[b] £ million current prices
Established			
Argyll	41	26	25
Auk	49	27	84
Beryl	47	28	335
Brent	34	22	951
Claymore	58	42	419
Cormorant	27	18	68
Dunlin	38	25	346
Forties	58	36	1971
Heather	31	20	101
Montrose	27	11	40
Murchison UK	23	15	40
Ninian	30	19	525
Piper	72	48	894
Statfjord UK	30	21	148
Thistle	38	23	398
Potential			
Beatrice	44	35	154
Cormorant Extension	29	22	144
Magnus	38	29	183
Tartan	33	25	120

[a] See p. 87.
[b] At a 20 per cent discount rate.
SOURCE Authors' estimates.

Before comments are made on the results in Table 4.5, some of the assumptions used in the calculations need more explanation.

(i) The estimates of internal rates of return (IRR) and net present value (NPV) are for projects funded without recourse to interest-bearing debt: if the financing schemes so far arranged for a number of projects were included, the NPV figure would be somewhat lower.

(ii) Royalties are based on the tax reference price with a nominal reduction in the rate of royalty to allow for cost of transport to land. PRT is calculated according to Oil Taxation Act (1975) provisions: tax liability is determined every six months and paid one period in arrears subject to the overriding operation of the 'annual limit clause'. All capital costs (see Table 4.2) are set against tax in the year in which they were incurred and a 75 per cent 'uplift' is applied to all such items. For Corporation Tax the individual field is taken as the unit of tax assessment: tax is assumed to be paid one period in arrears.

(iii) A discount rate of 20 per cent is applied to all net cash flows in order to calculate net present values in current prices (not real terms).[7] Whereas net present values are only shown in Table 4.5 in current prices, internal rates of return are calculated in both current and real (1977 price) terms by deflating net cash flows by the forecasts of the index of wholesale prices of manufactured products given in note 4.

(iv) The calculations are sensitive to the costs used, as well as to the output, tax and price assumptions which are varied in later chapters. It is difficult to know by how much one might reasonably expect costs to diverge from those assumed in this chapter. It can be demonstrated that small variations in rates of cost inflation (say $\pm$ 2 per cent) do not greatly affect rates of return. However, one or more step changes in costs, one way or the other, could have a substantial impact on the returns quoted.

Table 4.5 suggests that there is great variability among North Sea fields in terms of likely profitability, partly because of the substantial cost differences explained earlier in this chapter. Most of the internal rates of return, even when converted to real terms, will appear high to those used to the returns common in British manufacturing industry.[8] They do not, however, appear particularly high by global oil industry standards – and, of course, oil companies have to compare investment opportunities in the North Sea with those elsewhere in the world when deciding how to allocate their funds among competing uses. The relevant opportunity cost of capital is by no means clear. The 20 per cent in current price terms used in the NPV calculations may well be too low. Perhaps 20 per cent in real terms would be nearer the mark:[9] it will be seen that all of the projects except Montrose and Murchison UK achieve a real IRR of the order of 20 per cent or more.

In comparing profitability measures across fields, it is, of course, important to bear in mind the well-known problems of comparisons which use only internal rates of return when projects have different lives, different expenditures and different time-profiles of cash flows: North Sea fields differ in all these respects. Some of the fields with relatively high internal rates of return are small, short-life projects (such as Argyll and Auk) which have quite small net present values. One should look both at the internal rate of return and at the net present value in order adequately to assess the value of a field as an investment project.

NOTES AND REFERENCES

1. *Economic Trends* (London: Central Statistical Office, H.M. Stationery Office, July 1977), Appendix Table 1.
2. The cost estimates presented in this chapter are necessarily rather approximate assessments of aggregate costs for particular fields, but it should be pointed out that in practice cost estimates and cost control for North Sea projects are performed in a much more sophisticated fashion. In the case of the Thistle field, for example, during a two-and-a-half-year project support programme the project managers . . . purchased more than $540 million worth of equipment and materials and expedited its delivery to 55 locations in 7 countries. They provided construction management at 24 sites where components were fabricated, at Graythorp [where the production platform was constructed] and at 10 sites where production equipment modules were fabricated . . . At one time they were processing 2800 invoices a month and disbursing more than $1 million a day in as many as 14 currencies. *Petroleum Times*, London, 6–20 August, 1976, p. 11.
3. *North Sea Costs Escalation Study*, Department of Energy Paper No. 7 (London: H.M. Stationery Office, 1976) p. 109.
4. The cost estimates form part of a comprehensive series developed by the authors for both the established and potentially commercial North Sea oilfields. The estimates have been regularly brought up to date and are derived from both published sources of information and discussions with oil companies. Initially, they are made in 1977 prices and are then escalated by a forecast for the rate of change in the wholesale price of manufactured goods to derive cost estimates in current, that is money-of-the-day, terms. The forecasts of the UK wholesale price index are as follows:

	percentage change in index of wholesale prices of all manufactured products (home sales)
1976	16.4
1977	16.0
1978	10.0
1979	8.0
1980	7.0
1980–2000	6.0 (% p.a. compound rate of increase)

Source for 1976 index number: *Economic Trends* (London: Central Statistical Office, H.M. Stationery Office, May 1977), Table 42. Forecasts are authors' estimates.
5. *Noroil*, Stavanger, June 1977, pp. 49–56, for a review of sub-sea production techniques.

6. See also R. F. Hayllar and R. T. Pleasance, *UK Taxation of Offshore Oil and Gas* (London: Butterworths, 1977).

7. It is explained in Chapter 6 that, given the inflation assumptions used here, a 20 per cent discount rate in terms of current prices is approximately equivalent to a real discount rate of 11–13 per cent. The same convention of using a 20 per cent discount rate is employed in calculating net present values in Chapters 5, 6 and 7, but internal rates of return are also shown in most cases so that the reader can apply his own cut-off rate of return if he wishes. See note 9 below.

8. See, for example, *Bank of England Quarterly Bulletin*, London, June 1977, pp. 156–60. The North Sea returns in Table 4.5 are only on development and attributable exploration costs: if allowances could be made for other company costs they would be much reduced. The appropriate method of converting rates of return to real terms is also open to question. If, instead of using a general price index, one could use a specific index of North Sea replacement costs it is very likely that real returns would appear much lower than in Table 4.5. Unfortunately, no such index is available, although it is almost certainly true that North Sea capital costs have risen faster in recent years than prices in general.

9. A DCF cut-off rate of 25 per cent in real terms after tax is suggested as the target rate of major oil companies in the House of Commons Select Committee on Nationalised Industries, First Report Session 1974–75, *Nationalised Industries and the Exploitation of North Sea Oil and Gas* (London: H.M. Stationery Office, 1975) para 139. See also the discussion in Chapter 6 (pages 118–19).

CHAPTER 5

Tax Systems for North Sea Oil in Britain and Norway

The impact of the British offshore oil taxation system on company rates of return is examined implicitly at various places in this book.[1] In Chapters 4 and 6 rates of return are estimated on several price assumptions and in Chapter 7 the effect on profitability of depletion controls is discussed: since all the net present value and internal rate of return computations are *after tax* (that is, after royalties, Corporation Tax and Petroleum Revenue Tax) the taxation system figures in all these calculations. In this chapter, however, the impact of the United Kingdom taxation regime on company profitability and government revenues is investigated more explicitly and compared with the corresponding regime in Norway.[2] An introduction to the taxation system for United Kingdom offshore oil appears in Chapter 4 and in Chapter 9 there are some comments on the overall size of British government revenues from oil.

Despite the enormous rise in the cost of extracting North Sea oil – from early estimates of less than $1 per barrel to projections of $8–10 per barrel (£5–6 per barrel at $1.70 = £1) for the smallest new fields – there is still for many fields a large margin between the ruling price and total costs. For example, the established Forties field has estimated undiscounted total capital and operating costs measured at historic (not replacement) value, of about £1.4 per barrel (see Chapter 4): thus the margin between undiscounted costs per barrel and the 1977 price of $14.5 (£8.5) per barrel is about £7 per barrel. However, royalties, Corporation Tax and Petroleum Revenue Tax in total may eventually bring in over two-thirds of the pre-tax margin – in the case of Forties for example, up to 75 per cent of net revenues could accrue to the Government.

The study of the tax system is divided into two parts: in the first the United Kingdom oil taxation system is compared with its somewhat simpler Norwegian counterpart. Both systems include a new tax introduced specifically to deal with so-called 'excess profits' on North Sea operations: the Petroleum Revenue Tax and Special Tax. Norwegian oil policy, however, has up to now had rather different objectives since the country is already guaranteed substantial surplus supplies above self-sufficiency from just two established commercial fields — Statfjord and Ekofisk. As will be seen, therefore, the Norwegian tax structure was not evolved specifically to encourage the development of high unit cost fields.

In the concluding section of this chapter, some specific features of the British system are considered in more detail. Tax systems are rarely simple but the legislation covering the taxation of United Kingdom North Sea oil (the Oil Taxation Act, 1975) is quite extraordinarily complex and the enthusiasm of the authorities for eliminating potential loopholes may well cause practical problems. Although the existing system can be criticised,[3] the authorities will no doubt be reluctant to scrap it in the near future in favour of some theoretically more elegant solution. Nor does there appear to be much interest in official quarters in raising revenues by auctioning production licences (see Chapter 9) despite the powerful arguments in favour of such a system. Experience suggests that tax systems are usually improved by a series of modest amendments rather than frequent major upheavals: thus it is to the practical operation of the system rather than to underlying principles that the final part of the chapter is addressed.

THE BRITISH AND NORWEGIAN TAX STRUCTURES

ROYALTIES AND CORPORATION TAXES

In both the United Kingdom and Norway the prime sources of direct government revenues from North Sea operations are royalties, Corporation Tax and the new taxes levied specifically on offshore oil operations. In the United Kingdom the new tax is known as Petroleum Revenue Tax (PRT) and in Norway the Special Tax (ST).

Royalties are a simple barrelage tax traditionally imposed on the oil's wellhead value. For land-based operations where 'arm's length' sales take place, it is relatively easy to determine the tax reference value. But the great bulk of North Sea sales valuation is most likely to be where the oil is landed in the United Kingdom and not the wellhead. Under British production licences granted in the first four rounds of licensing and under all Norwegian licences so far granted, royalties are paid on the wellhead value of production and so it is necessary to calculate the costs of transporting oil to the point of known (sales) valuation so that a netback price to the wellhead may be determined. The manner in which transport costs to shore are treated for royalty purposes — whether subject to an immediate write-off, straight-line depreciation or equal instalments – and indeed exactly what costs should be allowed has already been the subject of disagreement between the British Government and the oil companies. Negotiations over allowable transport costs for the southern North Sea gas fields discovered in the mid-1960s were apparently still continuing a decade later. This no doubt prompted the Government to amend the regulations in 1976 in such a way that, for all licences granted under the fifth (and probably all future) rounds, royalties are to be levied on the tax reference or landed price. In the calculations which follow, therefore, the fifth-round terms are assumed since the aim is to determine what impact the tax system may have on future North Sea supplies. [4] The rate of royalty is 12.5 per cent of the tax reference price for all fields. Under the Norwegian system, the rate of royalty depends on the production volume and the period in which the licence was issued although some older licences have a fixed rate of 10 per cent. A sliding scale based on the tax reference price is assumed in this study. [5]

In the United Kingdom a Corporation Tax of 52 per cent applies to company profits, including those of companies operating in the North Sea. In Norway there are three main corporate taxes to consider: the Federal Tax of 26.5 per cent on corporate profits, a Municipality Tax of 24.3 per cent also on corporate profits, and a witholding tax of 10 per cent on distributed dividends. Expenditure may be deducted over a period of not less than six years from and including the year in which the asset comes into ordinary use. The deduction of tax-allowable losses is subject to the following two rules:

(i) Losses incurred may be carried forward for no more than fifteen years.

(ii) Only one-third of previous years' losses may be used in any particular year.

Although in the Norwegian legislation there is no exact counterpart of the 'ring fence' around United Kingdom oil-extraction activities (see Chapter 4), deduction of expenditures incurred outside the country from the profits of such operations is prohibited. Only 50 per cent of the losses from other petroleum and related activities either on shore or offshore can be deducted from the profits. Finally, distributed dividends are deductible from tax liability. This is a particularly important concession since, as is shown below, a wide range of company returns is possible depending on the extent to which dividends are distributed or profits retained.

PETROLEUM REVENUE TAX (PRT) AND THE SPECIAL TAX

The structure of PRT is explained briefly in Chapter 4. Here the tax is contrasted with its Norwegian counterpart, the Special Tax (ST).

PRT is defined in the United Kingdom Oil Taxation Act, 1975, and the rate was fixed at 45 per cent on the specially determined taxable profits from each oilfield. The profits are calculated after deducting allowable losses and, where applicable, a share of the revenue equivalent of a production allowance. PRT is levied twice yearly and the tax is payable four months after the close of each period. PRT may be deducted from profits in calculating Corporation Tax liability.

The Norwegian Special Tax was introduced in Odelsting Proposition No. 26 in February 1975. Like PRT, the legislation was enacted in 1975 but (unlike PRT) ST is levied on the same profits as are liable for Norwegian corporation taxes. As such, the Special Tax approximates to an 'excess profits' tax levied (after deduction of a special allowance) at the rate of 25 per cent and calculated on a company rather than a field basis. Extraneous losses, however, cannot be offset against the profits of Continental Shelf operations and since capital allowances may not be claimed until the asset is brought into 'ordinary use' ST assessment is effectively on a field-by-field basis.

THE TAX STRUCTURES COMPARED

In Chapter 2 major differences in offshore policy between the United Kingdom and Norway are described; these have had important consequences for the shaping of the two countries' tax systems. Whereas in the United Kingdom policy was guided by the desire for revenues to offset rapidly growing balance-of-payments deficits, in Norway the early discovery of substantially greater quantities of oil than were necessary to achieve self-sufficiency and a general distrust of the impact of oil on the economy discouraged any preferential treatment for high-cost fields. The United Kingdom system, in contrast, underwent substantial modification as it was passing through Parliament, specifically in an attempt to provide for a lower tax burden on high unit cost fields. But, despite the different final structures of the two systems, it will be seen that they produce remarkably similar results over a wide range of assumptions. In the following analysis, use is made of four of the five hypothetical field models[6] used in Chapters 3 and 4 with recoverable reserves respectively of 200, 300, 400 and 700 million barrels (referred to as the 200, 300, 400 and 700 fields in the rest of this chapter). The models were discussed in detail in Chapter 4, where Table 4.3 provides a year-by-year summary of the relevant production, operating and capital cost data. It must be emphasised that the models are based on the output and cost assumptions explained in Chapters 3 and 4: consequently they do not take into account the effects of depletion controls (see Chapter 7) or sharp changes in costs.

Table 5.1 compares internal rates of return (IRR) and net present

TABLE 5.1 Comparative After-tax Field Profitability and Government Take under the UK and Norwegian Tax Systems for Base Case[a]

Model field	United Kingdom system				Norwegian system[d]				Difference (UK less Norway)			
	IRR (%)	NPV[b] (£ million)	Government share of revenue[c] (%)	PRT share of revenue (%)	IRR (%)	NPV[b] (£ million)	Government share of revenue[c] (%)	ST share of revenue[c] (%)	IRR (percentage points)	NPV[b] (%)	Government share of revenue[c] (percentage points)	PRT/ST share of revenue[c] (percentage points)
200	25	32	66.6	6.3	22	14	66.7	13.4	3	56	−0.1	−7.1
300	16	−26	62.5	1.0	16	−29	59.7	8.9	0	12	2.8	−7.9
400	16	−36	61.6	0.5	16	−37	60.1	9.6	0	3	1.5	−9.1
700	13	−116	62.6	0.0	13	−117	58.0	5.1	0	1	4.6	−5.1

[a] North Sea oil price is $14.50 per barrel; Corporation Tax, PRT, royalty and Special Tax rates remain as in 1977. DCF returns are in money (not real) terms.
[b] At a 20 per cent discount rate.
[c] As percentage of net revenue (gross company revenue less capital and operating costs).
[d] For projects where the maximum amount of net income is distributed as dividends. The following figures apply when no dividend distribution is made:

	IRR (%)	NPV (£ million)	Government revenue (%)
200	20	−1	73.2
300	14	−40	67.3
400	14	−49	67.6
700	12	−134	65.6

SOURCE Authors' estimates.

values (NPV) – in both cases after tax – for the four fields under the 'base case' assumptions that the projects are funded entirely without interest-bearing debt, that the North Sea oil price remains constant at $14.50 per barrel, and that tax and royalty rates remain as in 1977. Government 'take' percentages are also shown. A constant money price is taken rather than one of the price scenarios used in Chapters 4 and 6, because it is then easier to compare the price-sensitivity of the returns with the effects on returns (at a constant price) of changes in tax rates and other variables. The rates of return quoted in this chapter are all in current price (not real) terms since they are based on the cost estimates of Chapter 4 which attempt to include future inflation.[7]

It is clear from Table 5.1 that, over a wide range of field sizes, rates of return on individual projects are similar under the two tax systems. Only in the case of the 200 field does profitability appear to be significantly higher under the British regime. The returns are also low enough to make the projects appear to be 'marginal' investments at the $14.5 price, emphasising the critical importance of price *expectations* for future North Sea supplies (see Chapter 6). Even the 200 field's internal rate of return of 25 per cent in current prices, which is equivalent to 16–18 per cent in real terms on the inflation assumptions used in Chapters 4 and 6, may be below the target rates of potential producing companies; moreover, it is based on technical advances which may not be introduced for some years yet. Two other features of Table 5.1 require some explanation. First, the share of PRT in the overall government revenue is much lower than ST because, for the model fields considered, the oil allowance and the annual limit formula (see Chapter 4) substantially reduce or eliminate the tax liability under the United Kingdom system, whereas ST is essentially additional to other taxes on corporate profits. But although PRT liability is virtually zero under the United Kingdom system, except for the 200 field the Government's share of revenue is consistently higher than under the Norwegian system. This is partly because the effective royalty rate is higher under United Kingdom rules, but a much more significant difference exists between the effective rates of corporation tax. For the 300 field, for example, the United Kingdom rate on net revenues is over 51 per cent compared with a 41 per cent Norwegian rate. The difference is mainly attributable to the ability to offset dividends against Federal tax liabilities in Norway. Where no dividend distribution takes place the Norwegian government share is substantially increased (footnote to Table 5.1) and for all field sizes is much higher than government 'take' under the British system.

SENSITIVITY ANALYSES: TAX RATE

Given this basic comparison between the United Kingdom and

Norwegian tax systems, one can now consider the effects of tax rate or price changes.

Figures 5.1 (i) to 5.1 (iii) contrast the effects of changing the PRT or ST rate under the two systems for the 200, 300 and 400 field models (the 700 – the least profitable of the model fields – pays no PRT under the base case). The diagrams demonstrate, for example, that *for a given price level* ($14.50 per barrel) the prospects for increasing the British Government's share of the net company revenues by raising the rate of PRT are limited: the annual limit on PRT (see Chapter 4) places an effective ceiling on percentage Government take. Increases in the Special Tax rate, however, will readily increase the Norwegian Government's share of net revenues because ST is nearer to an additional tax on corporate profits than is PRT. In general, for any given change in the rate of tax, the British Government's take alters relatively little and the impact on the after tax internal rate of return (in money terms) under the United Kingdom system is much less than under the Norwegian system.

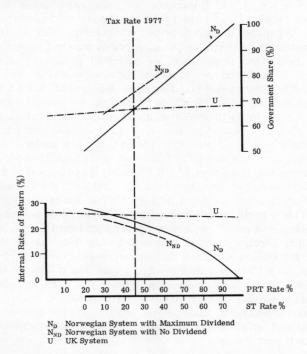

N_D Norwegian System with Maximum Dividend
N_{ND} Norwegian System with No Dividend
U   UK System

F_{IG} 5.1(i)   Internal Rates of Return and Government Shares of Net Company Revenues at Various Tax Rates: the 200 Field

SOURCE Authors' estimates.

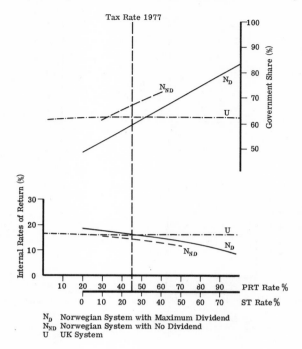

Fig 5.1(ii) Internal Rates of Return and Government Shares of Net Company Revenues at Various Tax Rates: the 300 Field

SOURCE Authors' estimates.

Figure 5.2 provides a separate statement of the relationship between the tax rate and the shares of net revenue taken by PRT and Special Tax. As the PRT rate increases, its share of net revenues soon reaches a low plateau for the 300 and 400 fields. In the case of the 200 field, the PRT share is more sensitive to the rate, but not nearly as sensitive as is the share of ST under the Norwegian system: a doubling of the ST rate approximately doubles its share of net revenues. It will be seen that, for the model fields examined here and at the 1977 price, PRT is a fairly small constituent of total government revenues. Table 5.1 shows that British Government 'take' (percentage of net company revenues) from the model fields from all taxes and royalties at 1977 rates is in the range 61–67 per cent; PRT at the 1977 rate, however, takes only between 0 and 15 per cent (Figure 5.2) of net company revenues. The maximum PRT take (from the 200 field) is only some 22 per cent.

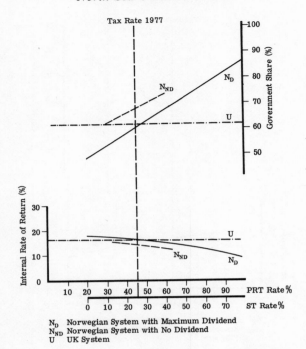

FIG 5.1(iii)   Internal Rates of Return and Government Shares of
                Net Company Revenues at Various Tax Rates: the 400 Field

SOURCE Authors' estimates.

SENSITIVITY ANALYSES: PRICE

The sensitivity analyses of tax rate changes at a fixed price given in
Figures 5.1 and 5.2 may be compared with an assessment of the effects of
price changes with the tax rate held constant (Figures 5.3 (i)–(iv)). All
tax rates are assumed to remain as they were in 1977 (including Special
Tax at 25 per cent and PRT at 45 per cent).

The general effect is for after-tax project returns to be marginally
lower under the United Kingdom tax regime at prices below the 1977
levels, except for the 200 field which at all prices is more profitable under
the British tax system, and for British Government 'take' to be
significantly greater at such prices. At higher prices projects tend to be
more profitable under the British system but — except for the 200 field —
the difference is small. These observations apply to comparisons with
Norwegian projects where the maximum permissible dividend is
declared (N_D); with no dividend distribution (N_{ND}), returns under the

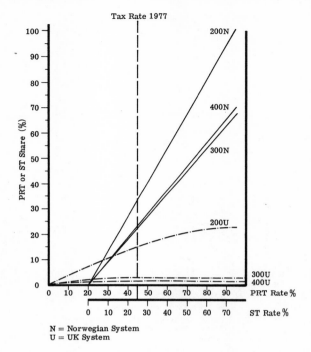

Fig 5.2   Special Tax and PRT Shares of Net Company Revenues at Various
Tax Rates by Field Size

SOURCE Authors' estimates.

Norwegian system would be reduced below those of United Kingdom
projects except possibly at the lowest prices considered.

It is surprising to find that the United Kingdom system, with
provisions evidently intended to safeguard against the effect of an oil
price decline, actually gives lower returns than the Norwegian regime in
such a situation. Similarly, as oil prices fall below the 1977 level, Figure
5.3 shows that, according to these calculations, the Government's share
of net revenues under the United Kingdom system increases and
significantly exceeds government share under the Norwegian system.
Figure 5.4 suggests that at such price levels there would be no PRT
liability; so as explained earlier, it is the combination of higher effective
royalty and corporation tax rates which determines the British
Government's share. At the lowest prices, royalties are the most
important source of revenue: at $10 per barrel, for example, under the
British system the 200 field has an internal rate of return of 15 per cent,

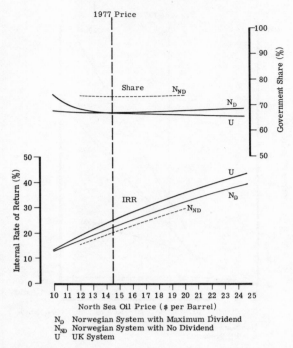

Fɪɢ 5.3(i)   Internal Rates of Return and Government Shares of Net Company
             Revenues at Various Prices: the 200 Field

sᴏᴜʀᴄᴇ Authors' estimates.

the Government takes three quarters of the net revenues, there is no
PRT liability (see Figure 5.4, where it is shown that PRT payments are
zero at $11 per barrel), royalties amount to £140 million and Corpor-
ation Tax to £180 million. At $8 per barrel the royalty element would be
£110 million and Corporation Tax £90 million.

SENSITIVITY ANALYSES: INTEREST-BEARING DEBT

When the United Kingdom Oil Taxation Act was debated in Parliament, it was claimed that the proposals to exclude all financing charges
from the costs chargeable in assessing PRT liability would seriously
damage profitability. In response to this claim, an additional (25 per
cent) uplift on allowable capital expenditure was introduced during the
Bill's passage. Since financing charges are allowable in Norway, it is
worth comparing the performance of the two systems for projects
partially funded from interest-bearing debt.

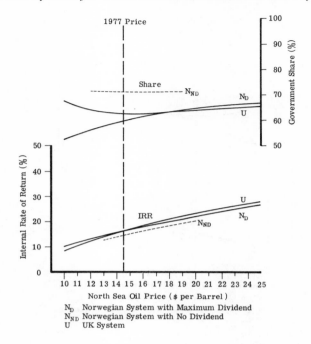

F$_{IG}$ 5.3(ii)   Internal Rates of Return and Government Shares of Net Company
Revenues at Various Prices: the 300 Field

s$_{OURCE}$ Authors' estimates.

The precise manner in which companies raise money for North Sea expenditure varies depending on the size of the company, the attractiveness of the project and market conditions in general. As a particularly severe sensitivity test the method of loan financing (which is the same in both sectors) adopted for the calculations shown in Figure 5.5 is as follows:

(*a*) The company's share of development finance is paid first. Loans finance all subsequent development costs.

(*b*) All loans are repaid within six years from the start of production. This is a rather restrictive assumption since a loan might otherwise be assumed to be repaid according to the timing of borrowing.

(*c*) Up to 75 per cent of net cash flow may be used in any year for repayment. Again, alternative less restrictive assumptions could include a repayment schedule which gradually builds up with production.

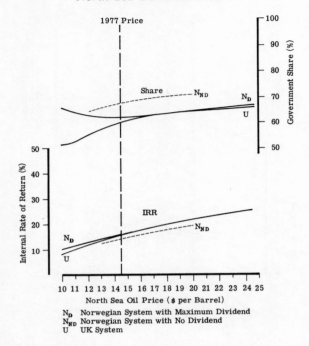

F_{IG} 5.3(iii)   Internal Rates of Return and Government Shares of Net Company
Revenues at Various Prices: the 400 Field

SOURCE Authors' estimates.

(*d*) The interest on all loans outstanding is levied at the rate of 10
per cent. Interest due on pre-production loans is capitalised.

1977 tax rates and a North Sea oil price of $14.5 per barrel are assumed.

The calculations demonstrate, as one would expect, that the government share of net revenues is lower under the Norwegian system than
under the British system on all debt-financed projects and that the
difference increases with the borrowing percentage. Only the 200 and
400 fields are shown in Figure 5.5 but similar conclusions apply to the
300 and 700 fields. The reason for the difference is the exclusion of
interest charges as allowances in the calculation of PRT assessable
profits whereas such charges are deductible under the Norwegian system
for both ST and Corporation Tax. For example, with 80 per cent
borrowing, government take under the British system is higher by about
3 percentage points for the 200 field and by about 6 percentage points for

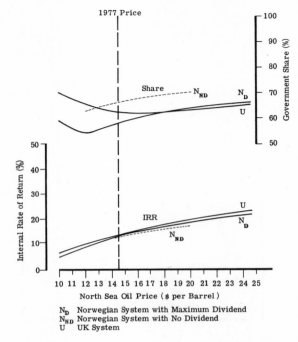

F<small>IG</small> 5.3(iv)   Internal Rates of Return and Government Shares of Net Company
Revenues at Various Prices: the 700 Field

<small>SOURCE</small> Authors' estimates.

the 400 field. With zero debt finance there is little difference in
government takes from the two fields under the two tax systems.

BRITISH AND NORWEGIAN TAX SYSTEMS: SOME CONCLUSIONS

Before examining some of the special features of the United Kingdom
tax system the following conclusions can be drawn from the sensitivity
studies.

(a) At 1977 prices and tax rates the Norwegian and United
Kingdom tax systems for offshore operations will probably yield
similar percentage government takes.

(b) PRT seems likely to be a relatively minor revenue raiser at the

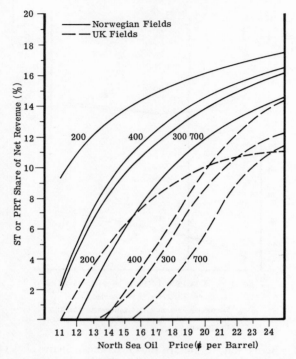

FIG 5.4 Special Tax and PRT Shares of Net Company Revenues at Various Prices

SOURCE Authors' estimates.

1977 price, and may well be zero or near zero for the higher-cost fields as was presumably the intention.

(*c*) The structure of PRT limits the scope for varying revenues under the United Kingdom system simply by manipulating the rate of tax. For instance, if the Government wants to increase its revenues from offshore oil it will either have to alter the safeguards or increase the royalty rate, in the absence of an increase in the rate of Corporation Tax (which would affect all industry). Norwegian government take, by contrast, is readily varied by altering the rate of Special Tax which is a closer approximation to a tax on 'excess profits' than is PRT.

(*d*) The higher effective royalty and Corporation Tax rates under the United Kingdom system may seriously reduce the effectiveness of the safeguards available under PRT. If prices were to fall substantially, for example, royalties would become a major element of

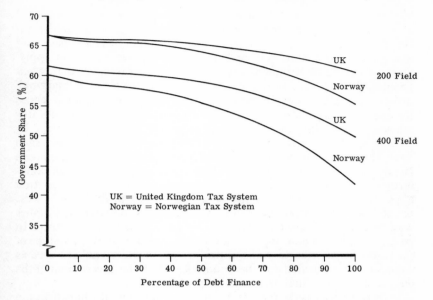

Fɪɢ 5.5 Government Shares of Net Company Revenues at Various Debt
Finance Percentages

sᴏᴜʀᴄᴇ Authors' estimates.

government revenue and the British system would be likely to yield
lower company returns and higher government takes than the
Norwegian system.

(*e*) The above conclusions refer to equity financed projects. Under
a debt-financing regime, substantial differences could arise between
the results of the two systems because the PRT legislation does not
allow interest payments and other financing charges to be offset
against profits as they are in the Norwegian system. Consequently, the
higher the proportion of debt finance, the lower would government
take seem likely to be under the Norwegian system as compared with
the British.

OPERATION OF THE BRITISH OIL TAXATION
SYSTEM IN PRACTICE

This chapter now turns to some of the unique features of the United
Kingdom oil taxation system. It will be recalled from Chapter 4 that, as
originally proposed, PRT would have been a relatively straightforward

levy on profits specially defined for the purpose with an additional allowance for qualifying capital expenditure. The two cardinal principles of PRT were that it should be levied on a field-by-field basis and that the normal definition of profits for tax purposes would not apply. So rigid was the Government's adherence to these principles that, when persuaded of the need to reduce the tax burden on so-called 'marginal' prospects, rather than relaxing either of its two principles it chose instead to accommodate such fields by granting a fixed tax-free allowance to participants related to production from each field and by placing a limit on the amount of PRT payable in any year from each field. These concessions were introduced at such a late stage that one can hardly suppose much time was available for consideration of their long-term effects. At the time the Government's major preoccupation appears to have been with the much publicised problem of 'excess profits' (see Chapter 9): the inclusion of measures to maximise supplies was, at least initially, considered to be of secondary importance. In passing, it is worth pointing out that the introduction of PRT as a type of excess profits tax creates something of precedent which could be used as a model for taxes levied on other industries which the government of the day declares to be making excessive profits.[8]

Such principles aside, there is the practical question of what effect the tax system may have on the further development of offshore oil resources which, as suggested in Chapter 3, are likely to include fields of smaller average size and higher unit costs than the established commercial fields. Earlier in this chapter, it is shown that, at the 1977 tax rate and at 1977 oil prices, PRT liability is likely to be small for high-cost North Sea fields. In that sense PRT in itself is not a serious deterrent to field development (although even without it only the 200 field might be an attractive investment at the present oil price and this depends on future technical innovations).

The question arises, however, of whether there are means within the existing tax structure to encourage the development of marginal prospects should it seem desirable to do so. One possibility is for the Minister to use his discretionary power to waive all or part of royalties from a field, but since royalty revenues are to be made available as investment capital to BNOC through the National Oil Account, the Government is likely to be reluctant to take up such an option.[9] Alternatively, one can examine what flexibility a company has within the present tax regime to adjust its operations so as to improve the after-tax returns on its high-cost projects. This means considering costs and returns to a company from its *entire* North Sea operations rather than dealing with single fields, as in the earlier part of this chapter.

Consider, for example, the 'ring fence' rules for determining Corporation Tax liability. Under these, losses made on other parts of a company's operations cannot be offset against the profits of its United

Kingdom oil-extraction activities. Where a company has a profitable established commercial field in the North Sea, however, investing in a new field at a time when corporate ring fence tax liabilities would otherwise occur may appear more attractive to that company than the same field would to another investor with no established field. There may also be good technical reasons for a company with an established field to develop reserves which are closely associated with it. For example, an existing pipeline may be shared by two neighbouring fields and certain processing facilities may be common to both operations.

As a brief example which incorporates both the above ideas and illustrates some of the complex and perhaps unintended effects the tax system may have on future supplies of North Sea oil, consider the following case. A company is nearing the start of production from a medium-sized established commercial field. In the following description the Thistle field is used as a model *purely for illustrative purposes*. Thistle yields a money DCF rate of return of 38 per cent using the Crude Price Indexation price scenario and a net present value at a 20 per cent rate of discount of just under £400 million (Table 4.5). The company is assumed to be considering developing an outlying prospect containing 200 million barrels of recoverable reserves using the novel techniques described in Chapter 4 for the model field of this size. If it is assumed that the new project is taxed separately and that its costs are not reduced through association with the established field (that is, they are exactly as stated in Table 4.3) then its internal rate of return would be 33 per cent in money terms with a corresponding NPV of £77 million (Table 5.2). Bearing in mind the technological uncertainties involved in developing the new field, a company anticipating such a return might consider it inadequate (see note 9, Chapter 4).

If the same company owns both fields, however, it will be assessed for Corporation Tax on its total profits from the two. The 'corporate return' for Case 1 in Table 5.2 analyses the effect of assessing Corporation Tax on the two fields together. In Case 1, PRT is assumed still to be paid separately for each field and there are still assumed to be no cost savings from the association between the fields. Thus the difference between the Case 1 return and the sum of the 'established field' and 'new project' returns is purely a result of switching to a corporate assessment for Corporation Tax. The Case 1 internal rate of return is not the weighted average of the separate project returns but increases to about the same as the 38 per cent from the established field alone.[10] The Case 1 net present value (£499 million) also exceeds the sum of the two project net present values (£475 million).

The reason for the improvement can be found by examination of the tax payments given in Table 5.3. In Case 1 Corporation Tax payments are significantly deferred as compared with the aggregate of the single project assessments although the total amount eventually paid is the

TABLE 5.2 Tax Analysis of Single and Multiple Field Investment[a]
After-tax DCF Returns (current prices)

	Internal Rate of Return (%)	Net Present Value[b] (£ million)
Returns for projects taxed separately		
Established field	38	398
New project	33	77
Corporate returns (2 fields)		
Case 1[c]	38	499
Case 2[c]	39	499

[a] Crude Price Indexation Price Scenario.
[b] At a 20 per cent discount rate.
[c] In both cases, the two projects are assessed jointly for Corporation Tax; in Case 2 they are also assessed jointly for PRT. See text, pp. 109–12.

SOURCE Authors' estimates.

same. In the three years prior to the start of production in 1982 from the new field, Corporation Tax liabilities from the established field amount to about £550 million when the new projects are taxed separately. When the projects are taken together (the Case 1 column), however, investment in the new project reduces the tax liability by about a quarter in this period to under £420 million. Thus a continuing programme of investment (provided suitable projects are available) can, in practice, have a significant effect on profitability by deferring corporate tax liabilities into the future. Although, as explained in Chapter 4, Corporation Tax is calculated on a field basis in other parts of this book because there is insufficient information to do otherwise, it should be borne in mind that this procedure will tend to underestimate after tax profitability in cases where companies have several fields.

Unlike Corporation Tax, Petroleum Revenue Tax is calculated rigidly on a field-by-field basis so it might appear that no tax deferment of the kind just described is possible under present legislation although minor relaxations of the principle allow. for example, abortive exploration expenditure to be relieved against the tax. Nevertheless, there is some ambiguity over the definition of an oilfield for tax purposes. If it is taken to include satellite developments which share common facilities with the established field then PRT might also be postponed as investment takes place in the new project. The concessionary production allowance is granted at 10 million long tons *per field* and so having two separate allowances could in some circumstances be more beneficial than a

TABLE 5.3 Tax Analysis of Single and Multiple Field Investment[a]
Cash Flow Analyses

	Production		Company revenues		PRT		Corporation Tax			Cash flow		
	Established field	New project	Gross revenue	Net revenue	Projects taxed separately	Projects taxed as one field	Projects taxed separately	Projects taxed as one field Case 1	Case 2	Projects taxed separately	Projects taxed as one field Case 1	Case 2
	(thousand barrels per day)				(£ million)							
1972										−2	−2	−2
1973										−13	−13	−13
1974										−34	−34	−34
1975										−87	−87	−87
1976										−120	−120	−120
1977	10		31	7						−133	−133	−133
1978	125		409	316						273	273	273
1979	176		601	483						393	393	393
1980	200		721	587	109	9	179	144	143	171	206	306
1981	145		550	437	192	117	242	182	234	−69	−8	14
1982	124	45	670	524	150	144	128	90	129	227	264	231
1983	105	60	689	533	126	189	123	184	187	277	216	149
1984	89	60	654	502	104	190	136	208	175	262	190	137
1985	76	60	625	475	111	178	207	207	162	157	157	135
1986	65	52	571	427	115	159	189	189	154	123	123	114
1987	55	43	517	378	87	134	162	162	139	129	129	105
1988	47	36	468	334	60	108	151	151	127	123	123	99
1989	40	31	423	295	34	74	143	143	117	119	119	104
1990	34	26	383	260	12	40	136	136	115	112	112	104
Total	471	151	7312	5558	1100	1342	1796	1796	1682	1908	1908	1775
	(million barrels)											

[a] Crude Price Indexation Price Scenario

SOURCE Authors' estimates.

'corporate' assessment to PRT. But the other concession – the annual limit on tax payable – is related to historic investments and so it is conceivable that postponement of early tax payments and an increased investment allowance, because the two fields are treated as one, could reduce tax payments to a greater extent than they are increased through the loss of a production allowance.

In Table 5.2, the Case 2 corporate returns demonstrate the effect of treating the two fields as one for PRT purposes. All other assumptions are the same as in Case 1. It can be seen that on the assumptions specified here the company might have a slight preference for Case 2 as compared with Case 1. The internal rate of return is slightly higher in Case 2 but the net present value is virtually the same (the unrounded calculations show a fractional increase). From Table 5.3 it can be seen that total PRT liabilities increase (through the lower production allowance) but PRT in the first few years is smaller because investment in the new field postpones the onset of PRT payment. The lower PRT payments in the early years are to some extent offset by higher early year corporation tax payments but total corporation tax paid is less.

This simple example shows that there might be circumstances in which derogation of the field-by-field rule for PRT assessment could provide some additional incentive to develop so called 'marginal' prospects. Early experience suggests that in any case the definition of an oilfield for tax purposes is proving to be a more complex matter than the legislation implies. The definition is to be based purely on geological considerations, which are frequently imprecise and often call for arbitrary decisions on field boundaries. Consider for example the common situation in the North Sea where a field consists of two reservoirs at different depths separated by unproductive horizons: one reservoir lies on top of another. Are the two reservoirs to be considered as separate fields for tax purposes? If they are not (as seems to be the general assumption), then why are reservoirs separated geologically but in close geographical proximity to be considered as two discrete fields for such purposes?

The above example provides just one simple illustration of how the practice of the Oil Taxation Act (1975) will call for some interpretation of the 'national interest' by its executors, which is not a role which one presumes they either coveted or will enjoy. Similarly, one can expect the attitude of the various enterprises involved in North Sea development to vary enormously towards the Act. Such companies range from BNOC, which is not presently required to pay PRT, to the multinational companies which may have a programme of investments embracing several fields, to small participants who perhaps see returns from their North Sea ventures as bonuses to add to profits from onshore enterprises in unrelated areas. It will be surprising if the tax strategies of all three coincide happily: it will be even more surprising if the Oil

Taxation Act works in practice as smoothly as its proponents suggest it will.

NOTES AND REFERENCES

1. The methodology used in this chapter and some early results appeared in Morgan and Robinson, 'The Comparative Effects of the UK and Norwegian Oil Taxation Systems on Profitability and Government Revenue', *Accounting and Business Research*', Exeter, Winter 1976.
2. This chapter concentrates on the impact of the tax system on individual oilfield projects because the outside observer cannot know in detail the tax positions of the companies. But it would be wrong to picture the fiscal regime as one in which taxes are levied simply on a field-by-field basis. For want of better information, Corporation Tax is calculated in the first part of this chapter as though it were charged on individual fields rather than on companies but this inevitably introduces some error. In practice, a company will adjust its operations as best it can to the tax system (as to other aspects of the environment in which it operates). The last section of this chapter indicates how Corporation Tax payments on a corporate basis may differ from such payments on a field basis.
3. See Morgan, 'The Promise and Problems of Petroleum Revenue Tax', in *Proceedings of the Institute of Fiscal Studies Conference on the Taxation of North Sea Oil*, London, February 1976.
4. In Chapter 4, the profitability calculations for fields discovered under existing licences assume that royalties are assessed on wellhead value.
5. The Norwegian rate depends on the production volume and the period in which the licence was issued. Some older licences have a fixed rate of 10 per cent. The details of the sliding scale are as follows:

Average daily production	*Royalty percentage*
under 40,000 (barrels)	8
40,000 and under 100,000	10
100,000 and under 225,000	12
225,000 and under 350,000	14
350,000 and over	16

6. Model fields are used rather than actual British or Norwegian fields so as to analyse, for a field with specified characteristics, the effects on company returns and government revenues of the two tax systems.
7. See Chapter 4, notes 7 and 9, for comments on money and real rates of return, and Chapter 6 (pages 123–8) for a discussion of the impact on North Sea returns of price variations.
8. See J. Whalley, 'Economic Aspects of North Sea Oil Taxation', in *Proceedings of the Institute of Fiscal Studies Conference on the Taxation of North Sea Oil, op. cit.*
9. According to press reports, the operators of the Argyll field have applied for royalty remission. See the *Financial Times*, London, 31 August 1977.
10. The unrounded calculations actually show a slightly higher internal rate of return for Case 1 (38.4 per cent) than for the established field alone (38 per cent).

CHAPTER 6

World Oil Prices, Profitability and the Supply of North Sea Oil

SOME GENERAL CONSIDERATIONS

In Chapter 1 it was pointed out that North Sea oil producers are essentially price-takers: in the foreseeable future the price they obtain for their product will be determined by the price of OPEC crude oil (adjusted for location and quality differences). This chapter examines in some detail the effect of price on the profitability of North Sea oil, using as a basis the general analysis in Chapter 4 of rates of return on given assumptions about output, costs, tax rates and prices.[1] Some conclusions are also drawn about how profitability changes may affect the supply of North Sea oil.

The impact of price changes on North Sea profitability and supplies cannot be determined simply by estimating rates of return on complete oilfield projects (that is, on projects seen *ab initio*, by the potential producer) at varying price levels. The principal complications are as follows.

First, the effect of a price change on the profitability of and supplies from any given field will be to some extent dependent on the stage of development of that field. As shown in Chapter 3, fifteen British North Sea oilfields are under development (late 1977), of which six are actually producing oil; there appear to be another twenty-one developable fields which have been found but to which no capital other than exploration has been committed; and there are likely to be further discoveries as a result of future exploration. The effect of price variations is likely to differ among these three categories of field.

A North Sea oilfield development project is heavily 'front-end-loaded', to use the descriptive if inelegant title applied to investments where a comparatively high proportion of aggregate discounted costs is incurred in the early years. The project will normally have a long life compared with many manufacturing investments (probably twenty-five years from its start), a relatively high rate of return will be expected in line with the company's opportunity cost of capital, a great deal of capital will be spent before any revenue accrues, and the equipment will generally be very specific to the particular project. Consequently, a large proportion of the total discounted costs is sunk and becomes unavoidable fairly early in the project's life. After five or six years it is likely that the bulk of the investment will have been spent and that this, because of the high discount rate, will dominate total discounted project costs. The company will probably have fixed platforms on the field, and frequently a pipeline to shore also, which have little value in alternative uses. [2] Therefore, once a few years have passed the company is likely to foresee a revenue stream which is large relative to its avoidable costs (costs of operating the field and any further investment). Taking the Forties field as an example, the bulk of capital expenditure had probably been completed by the end of 1977 — about £640 million out of total estimated investment of just over £700 million. Revenues from oil production began only in late 1975 and only became substantial in 1977. When the field has reached its plateau level of output (probably in 1978), however, it should yield annual revenues of £1600 million or more for a few years, compared with annual costs (excluding taxes and royalties) of around £100 million.

Though Forties is likely to be a comparatively profitable field (see Chapter 4), it will be shown below that for all North Sea oilfields so far discovered the same general conclusion seems to apply — that, after five or six years into the project, future discounted revenues are likely to be high relative to future discounted costs. Thus a producer who considers returns on avoidable costs only, forgetting bygones, may be able to achieve acceptable rates of return on such avoidable future expenditures even at low levels of price. An important conclusion for the British North Sea area as a whole is that the supply curve of offshore oil (the relationship between price and quantity supplied) will shift according to the timing of any price changes. Take, for example, the effect of a reduction of 10 per cent in the world price of crude oil. The effect of such a change on North Sea supplies would most likely be quite different if it occurred in 1977 from what its effect would be in 1980 when more capital would have been committed and a greater proportion of field costs would therefore have become unavoidable.

The impact of price variations on the other two categories of field is, however, likely to be quite different. A company contemplating investment in

    (*a*) developing a field already discovered but on which only exploration funds have so far been spent
    (*b*) exploring for new fields

will consider likely returns on its full costs. That is, all costs (exploration in case (*b*) and in both cases development capital and operating) are avoidable. In such cases, companies will presumably be influenced in their investment decisions by expected returns on complete oilfield projects, though not necessarily at the existing price level; their price *expectations* will also be important.

There are some further complications which are mentioned below, although for various reasons they are not explicitly taken into account in the calculations of price effects. First, as explained in Chapter 2, a change in prices may well affect producers' price expectations and, as a consequence, induce them to change their depletion profiles. For example, if a producer came to believe that world oil prices would, in the future, rise at a rate exceeding his discount rate, he would have an incentive to hold back output (as compared with his original production programme) since in this way he could increase the expected net present value of his reserves. Similarly, an expected price decline would tend to increase his rate of depletion. Such desirable responses to changing market conditions will not be possible, or will at least be muted, in the British sector of the North Sea if the extensive depletion control powers of the Secretary of State for Energy (see Chapter 2) are maintained. In interpreting the calculations which follow it should be borne in mind that they assume that producers cannot, because of government controls, adjust production plans already agreed with the Department of Energy if their price expectations alter. A less regulated depletion regime in the British North Sea would clearly give the producers more opportunity to respond to price changes; for instance, it would allow them to adapt to actual and expected price reductions by expanding output and would thereby vitiate the effects of price declines on profitability as calculated in this chapter.

Finally, it should be pointed out that the estimates which follow only indicate broad orders of magnitude. Earlier chapters have explained the problems of estimating output, costs, tax rates and other relevant variables for a new petroleum province for many years into the future. Although one might argue that in estimating the effect of price variations one is more concerned with *changes* in rates of return and supplies than with the *levels* from which those changes originate, there are some additional complications in dealing with price changes which are difficult to quantify and which have been ignored in the calculations in this chapter. For example, it is quite likely that price changes will cause cost changes. If prices were to fall, producers might be stimulated into cutting costs, either on the basis of existing technologies or by the more rapid introduction of new ones (such as sub-sea completions). A related effect is that cost-cutting campaigns might result in lower recovery rates from given reserves-in-place. Similarly, price increases relative to costs might raise rates of recovery.

Two sets of calculations now follow. The first analysis is intended to quantify the effect of a price *decline* on the rates of return from fields already under development and to draw some general conclusions about how oil supplies from such fields might be affected. The second examines the impact of a number of price scenarios on the rates of return from complete oilfield projects and suggests how the various assumed future price trends might influence future exploration and development activity.

DEVELOPMENT OF EXISTING FIELDS

The reason for investigating the effect of a price decline is that there has been considerable discussion of the likely impact of such a decline in world oil prices on the profitability and hence on the supply of North Sea oil. Fears that OPEC prices might be significantly reduced — either through deliberate action by the oil producers or because of an outbreak of price-cutting — have led to various efforts to protect indigenous energy supplies in the industrialised world. The 'safeguard' provisions of the Petroleum Revenue Tax (see Chapters 4 and 5) and the Minister's discretionary power to remit royalties on North Sea production are United Kingdom examples. On the international scale, the International Energy Agency has reached an agreement in principle that there should be a $7 per barrel minimum price for imported oil[3] and there has been a long dispute within the European Community about whether or not to set a $7 minimum price for oil imported into the Community.[4]

To illustrate the effect of a price reduction on North Sea oilfields now under development, four fields with widely varying rates of return (Forties, Montrose, Dunlin and Thistle) are chosen. Recoverable reserves, the depletion profile over time and the costs for each field are shown in Chapters 3 and 4. Tax and royalty rates are assumed to remain as at present, as is the tax and royalty structure for offshore oil (explained in Chapters 4 and 5).

The procedure then adopted is to calculate for each field a 'required price' which indicates, at any given point in the field's life, what price is necessary in order to cover avoidable expenditures and yield an acceptable after tax return on these expenditures. Following the argument used earlier in this chapter, unavoidable (sunk) costs are ignored. Essentially, past expenditures and, where relevant, past revenues, are ignored, so that the comparison is between future expenditures and future revenues, suitably discounted. The method used is like that in the usual DCF calculation, where revenues and costs are given and the internal rate of return and net present value are calculated, except that in this case the rate of return is taken as given along with costs and quantities produced; it is price which is the unknown. The required price (p_r) is found by dividing the sum of the discounted relevant costs (ΣC_d) by the sum of the discounted relevant quantities (ΣQ_d).

$$\text{Thus, } p_r = \frac{\Sigma C_d}{\Sigma Q_d}.$$

In addition to the difficulties of estimating future costs and future quantities, a problem in this type of analysis is to determine what rate of discount to use. Since the opportunity cost of capital will vary among producing companies at any given time and for the same company over time[5] there is no way of arriving at an accurate value for 'the rate of discount' appropriate to British North Sea oil for the next twenty-five years. The approach used here is to make two sets of calculations to determine how robust are the conclusions with respect to variations in the discount rate. The first calculation assumes a minimum required internal rate of return (IRR) after tax of 20 per cent in terms of current prices (that is, without correction for general inflation).[6] An approximate adjustment for such general inflation, using forecasts of the United Kingdom wholesale price index for home sales of manufactured products, suggests that the corresponding real rate of discount is of the order of 11–13 per cent.[7] The calculations are repeated for a 30 per cent

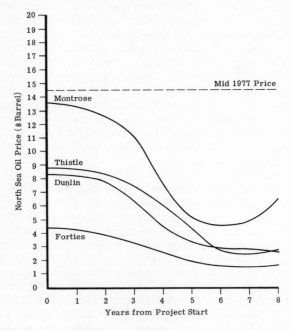

Fig 6.1   Prices at which Project Earns 20 per cent IRR (after tax) on Cash Flows from Given Years Onwards

SOURCE Authors' estimates.

IRR (approximately 20–23 per cent real rate of return) in order to investigate their sensitivity to variations in the discount rate.

Figure 6.1 and 6.2 demonstrate the results of the calculations, for 20 per cent IRR and 30 per cent IRR respectively. In each diagram the point at which the curve for a given field intersects the vertical axis gives the price which, *if maintained over the full life of the field*, would just yield the required IRR (20 per cent in Figure 6.1 and 30 per cent in Figure 6.2). The very large differences on each diagram between the required prices over the full field lives are, of course, consequences of the very considerable variations in the costs of the various fields. Forties, for example, on the assumptions used here, requires a constant North Sea oil price of only about $4.5 per barrel to achieve 20 per cent IRR (Figure 6.1) and $6.5 to achieve 30 per cent IRR (Figure 6.2), whereas the corresponding prices for Montrose appear to be about $13.5 and $17.5 per barrel. The price of North Sea oil in mid-1977 was of the order of $14.5 per barrel, as the diagrams show.

As one moves to the right in each diagram, the declining required prices which are indicated are those which would be needed in order to

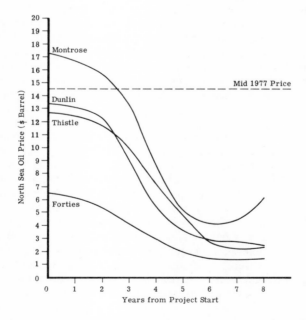

F<small>IG</small> 6.2   Prices at which Project Earns 30 per cent IRR (after tax) on Cash Flows from Given Years Onwards

SOURCE Authors' estimates.

achieve the given IRR *from that point in the project onwards* – ignoring all bygone costs and revenues. Naturally, since capital expenditures are concentrated during a few years early in the project, the effect up to about year 6 (year 0 being project start) is to remove large quantities of expenditure but not to change revenues: thus, the calculated required price drops sharply for the first few years of the project, then stabilises or increases slightly (because of increasing unit operating costs). For instance, Forties, which on these calculations requires a price of $6.5 to earn 30 per cent DCF after tax *on the whole project* would, after about six years of development, need a price of only $1.5 to $2 per barrel – that is, approximately the pre-October 1973 price – to earn 30 per cent *on avoidable expenditures from then on.* The required prices for Dunlin and Thistle are only about $1 per barrel higher than for Forties from year 6 onwards. Montrose, which is a relatively high-cost field, shows a similar time-pattern, although the required prices are greater. The conclusions are very robust with respect to the discount rate assumed. Using the 30 per cent IRR shifts the curves upwards in the early years but does not alter the broad message which can be derived from this analysis, the purpose of which is to quantify something which is fairly obvious intuitively. Given the concentration of capital spending in the early years of a field's development, even a large decline in OPEC prices, *once development is under way*, should have a relatively small effect on the output of that field. There might be some tendency for recovery rates to fall because of cost-cutting, but the essential point is that once a large amount of capital has been committed returns on incremental expenditures seem likely to appear high enough to producers, as compared to alternative spending opportunities, for them to continue producing even at very low prices by today's standards.

One can therefore draw the general conclusion that any likely reductions in world oil prices will probably not greatly affect North Sea oil output in the next few years since fields already under development (the established commercial fields of Chapter 3) should go ahead almost regardless of price. The producers are unlikely to walk away at any prices one can reasonably foresee. It is probable, therefore, that production from the fifteen established commercial fields – the lowest line in Figure 3.3 in Chapter 3 – will be insensitive to price fluctuations in the next five years or so. Later there could be some adverse effect on supplies if prices were to decline since, as the lives of fields advance, operating costs will tend to increase relative to revenues and the prices required by producers will rise quite sharply in some cases.

FUTURE EXPLORATION AND DEVELOPMENT ACTIVITY

It is quite a different story with fields on which development has not yet begun and those waiting to be discovered – the higher curves in Figure 3.3. In such cases the avoidable costs of potential producers include the full capital costs of development and, for reservoirs not yet discovered, exploration costs as well. Potential producers consequently have much more flexibility in determining their future supply behaviour, which is likely to be far more elastic with respect to price variations than is the case for fields already under development.

The subsequent analysis examines how rates of return *on total projects* are likely to vary with price. Following the analysis in Chapter 3, the investigation is based on three groups of fields: first, on the fifteen fields already being developed (the 'established commercial fields'); second, fields which have apparently been discovered but had not started development by 1977 ('potentially commercial fields'); and, third, future discoveries. As already explained, any cost and profitability calculations for the North Sea can, at the present stage of development, only give rough orders of magnitude. Obviously, the estimates given here for the second and third groups of fields are very tentative: they are intended only to indicate how potential producers might view such prospects.

In order to assess the impact on rates of return of future price variations, several price scenarios are used to represent different future states of the world oil market and to span a reasonably probable range of oil price movements. The use of scenarios, tied to specific assumptions about OPEC behaviour and other variables affecting the world oil market, seems a superior device to the alternative of assessing rates of return at various price levels. One of the few things which seems certain about future oil prices is that they will vary over time: there is thus little point in calculating what returns would be at various price levels held constant over field lives.

The three scenarios are in terms of *North Sea* oil prices but, since North Sea producers are assumed to be price-takers, they are based on assumed movements in world oil prices.[8] In mid-1977, the market price of Forties and Ekofisk crude oil appears to have been just below \$14.5 per barrel[9] – approximately the same as Nigerian crude, which is of similar gravity (37° API) to the North Sea crudes then being produced, though slightly lower in sulphur. The price of the Arabian Light 'marker' crude (34° API) at that time was \$12.70 per barrel, but North Sea oil has a substantial freight advantage and a lower sulphur content. The North Sea prices used in the scenarios, which start from a base of \$14.5 per barrel in mid-1977, are intended to represent the price of a *low-sulphur* crude such as Forties or Ekofisk. North Sea crude oils with higher sulphur content will generally command lower prices. The three scenarios are as follows.

1. Crude Price Indexation (CPI).
This is taken as the base scenario, not because it is the most likely but

because it appears to come closest to the present expectations of the companies operating in the North Sea. Essentially it is a 'surprise-free' scenario in which the world oil price rises at a steady rate of 5 per cent per annum between 1977 and 1985 and (because of increasing scarcity) at 7 per cent per annum from 1985 to 1995. A surprise-free projection may seem inappropriate in view of the large number of surprises the oil market has produced in recent years but CPI gives us a standard against which to judge the other scenarios. It is intended to represent, very roughly, an oil price rising at the same rate as the rate of increase of the price of world manufactured exports so that the terms of trade between the oil producers and the industrial countries remain approximately constant. CPI yields a North Sea oil price of over $21 per barrel in 1985 and $42 per barrel in 1995 (not corrected for inflation, of course) compared with $14.5 barrel in mid 1977.

2. *Limited Price Decline for a Limited Period (LPD)*.
In this scenario the members of OPEC are assumed to lose for a time their ability to make substantial increases in prices. Prices drift down gradually in the late 1970s, under the impact of open or concealed discounting, so that by 1980 the price of North Sea oil falls to $13 per barrel. Prices then rise a little in the early 1980s and more rapidly from the mid 1980s, as expectations of future scarcity induce the oil producers to hold back output and start another upward price movement which approximately doubles prices between 1985 and 1995. The North Sea oil price is $15 per barrel in 1985 and over $29 per barrel in 1995. Throughout the period OPEC remains in existence but it does not introduce an explicit output-sharing scheme and it becomes less cohesive as more countries join. Consequently there are no sharp price increases caused by the use of monopoly power.

3. *Use of Monopoly Power (UMP)*.
The UMP scenario begins with a smaller-scale repetition of the events of 1973. The oil producers conclude, on the basis of various statements made and reports written in the industrialised countries in the mid-1970s,[10] that oil will become significantly scarcer by the mid-1980s. As a result their reaction, as in the early 1970s (see Chapter 1) is to curtail output programmes and hold back barrels of oil for the presumed higher-priced future. Prices increase sharply: it is assumed here that the price of North Sea oil jumps about 25 per cent between 1977 and 1978, 10 per cent in 1979 and 10 per cent in 1980. Thereafter, it rises at an average compound rate of 7 per cent per annum until 1985: in 1986 there is a further 25 per cent increase, followed by an annual average compound rate of increase of 7 per cent until 1995. The price of North Sea oil is nearly $31 per barrel in 1985 and over $70 per barrel in 1995.

These three scenarios are by no means the extreme possibilities but they serve to illustrate how sensitive are the profitability of exploration and the development of North Sea fields to future price variations. Table 6.1 gives details of the assumed future prices.

A comparison of the results of applying these price scenarios is given in Tables 6.2 to 6.4. As with the earlier calculations in this chapter, the recoverable reserves, depletion profiles and costs for individual fields set out in Chapters 3 and 4 are used: tax and royalty rates and regimes are assumed to remain as now. No attempt has been made to calculate feedback effects into costs from variations in oil prices. To the extent that changes in world oil prices are positively correlated with rates of inflation in the industrialised countries, costs will probably rise faster in UMP and slower in LPD as compared with CPI: thus the actual improvement in North Sea profitability in UMP and the decline in LPD (both relative to CPI) will probably be somewhat less than shown in Tables 6.2 to 6.4.

TABLE 6.1 Assumed Future North Sea Oil Prices ($ per barrel)

| Mid-year | Price scenario | | |
	CPI	LPD	UMP
1977	14.5	14.5	14.5
1978	15.2	14.0	18.1
1979	16.0	13.5	19.9
1980	16.8	13.0	21.9
1985	21.4	15.0	30.7
1990	30.0	21.0	50.3
1995	42.1	29.5	70.5

CPI = Crude Price Indexation
LPD = Limited Price Decline
UMP = Use of Monopoly Power

SOURCE Authors' estimates.

In Table 6.2, estimated rates of return are given in real terms for the 15 fields already under development. Examining first the crude price indexation (CPI) scenario, which appears to approximate to the price expectations of many of the North Sea producers and which is used in the profitability analyses of Chapter 4, a striking feature of the table is the large differences in the calculated returns which stem from the widely varying characteristics of North Sea oilfields. Montrose and Murchison UK, for example, have relatively low anticipated real rates of return by normal oil-producing standards, whereas Claymore and Piper appear likely to yield very high returns. It is perhaps necessary to reiterate here the warning that all these estimates are based on forecasts for many

TABLE 6.2 The Sensitivity of Project Returns to Price: Fifteen Established Commercial Fields' Real Internal Rates of Return after Tax (percentage)[a]

Field	Price scenario[b]		
	CPI	LPD	UMP
Argyll	26	25	30
Auk	27	26	31
Beryl	28	23	34
Brent	22	17	28
Claymore	42	34	51
Cormorant	18	12	26
Dunlin	25	19	32
Forties	36	33	41
Heather	20	14	28
Montrose	11	5	17
Murchison UK	15	9	22
Ninian	19	14	25
Piper	48	43	55
Statfjord UK	21	16	28
Thistle	23	18	29

[a] Using the forecasts of the wholesale price index given in Note 4, ch. 4.
[b] See pp. 121–2.

SOURCE Authors' estimates.

years ahead of output, costs and tax rates: many things can happen in the next twenty five years to cause the outcome to differ from present forecasts.

The effect of a moderate price decline in the next few years followed by price rises in the 1980s (the LPD scenario) is to cut the CPI real rates of return on average by about 5.5 percentage points ($\pm$ 2 points). Exceptions are Argyll and Auk, which are expected to be much shorter-life fields than the others and which therefore are fairly insensitive to the price variations used. Real returns on Montrose, Murchison UK, Cormorant and possibly Heather, Ninian, Statfjord UK and even Brent decline, on the LPD scenario, to levels which the producing companies might well consider to be below the minimum acceptable if they could consider the projects *ex ante*.

In the UMP case, where there are assumed to be some substantial OPEC-induced price increases, the calculated real rates of return are considerably higher. Argyll and Auk apart, the average increase in real IRR in UMP as compared to CPI is of the order of 7 percentage points ($\pm$ 2 points). That is to say, the IRR increases in UMP relative to CPI are slightly greater than the IRR *decreases* in LPD relative to CPI. In

UMP, the calculated return on each field – with the possible exception of Montrose – appears to be sufficiently high that a potential oil producer, regarding such a project *ex ante*, would most likely to be prepared to invest in it.

Table 6.3 shows a similar analysis for a selection of fields discovered but not yet under development ('potentially commercial fields'). Unlike the fields in Table 6.2 the capital costs of the Table 6.3 fields (exploration and some preliminary development planning work apart) are avoidable so that the companies concerned will view them *ex ante* as complete investment projects. The estimates of real rates of return are obviously even more speculative than those in Table 6.2 and there is insufficient information for returns to be calculated for all the twenty-one discoveries mentioned in Chapter 3. In general, the rates of return appear to be of the same order of magnitude as those in Table 6.2, although there are no exceptionally high returns such as those for Piper and Claymore. All the fields would probably be regarded as reasonable development prospects on the CPI scenario.

TABLE 6.3 The Sensitivity of Project Returns to Price: Selected Potentially Commercial Fields' Real Internal Rates of Return after Tax[a] (percentage)

Field	Price scenario[b]		
	CPI	LPD	UMP
Beatrice	35	25	47
Cormorant Extension	22	16	30
Lyell	23	16	31
Magnus	29	21	40
Tartan	25	17	35
Tern	29	20	41

[a] Using the forecasts of the wholesale price index given in Note 4, ch. 4.
[b] See pp. 121–2.

SOURCE Authors' estimates.

A limited price decline – which reduces real IRRs by 8 ± 2 percentage points for the fields – might, however, place in doubt the development of Cormorant Extension, Lyell and Tartan. On the UMP scenario, which increases returns relative to CPI by about 10 ± 2 percentage points, all the Table 6.3 fields appear to be good investment projects.

Assumed future discoveries are considered in Table 6.4 using the five field size groups and types of development programme explained in Chapters 3 and 4. Obviously, the rates of return quoted are subject to wide error margins. Bearing in mind this qualification, it appears that there is no clear trend for profitability to vary directly with field size. On the CPI scenario the smallest fields (100 million barrels) do not look good prospects and there is some doubt about the 700 million barrel fields also; all the fields look doubtful investment projects on the LPD scenario; only if one assumes the UMP scenario do all the fields seem attractive investments.

CONCLUSIONS

At this early stage of development of the British North Sea it is not possible to calculate a supply schedule which demonstrates how oil supplies would be likely to vary with oil prices. This chapter has attempted, however, to analyse the supply-price problem, identifying those areas where supplies are likely to be price-sensitive and those where they are not. In the first part of the chapter it was pointed out that by using the distinction between avoidable and unavoidable costs one could divide North Sea oilfields into three categories. Supplies from the first category — established commercial fields — are probably not very sensitive to oil price variations because such a large proportion of their costs is already unavoidable.

The fields from which future supplies are likely to be most sensitive to price changes are those listed in Tables 6.3 (discovered but not under development) and 6.4 (undiscovered). According to the estimates made in this chapter, if world oil prices were to fall moderately in the next few years, even though the oil companies expected them to rise again in the 1980s and 1990s (which is the implication of the LPD scenario) their anticipated real internal rates of return would decline quite sharply as compared with the CPI scenario (taken to be the companies' present expectation). Consequently, many of the fields already discovered but not under development (Table 6.3) would look a good deal less attractive than they now appear. Development delays would most likely ensue in such circumstances, particularly since there would be increased uncertainty about future price movements: for example, if there were a price reduction the companies might expect prices to remain depressed longer than the LPD scenario assumes so that their *anticipated* returns would be less than shown in Table 6.3, whatever their *actual* returns might turn out to be. For these reasons, it seems probable that though a modest price decline would leave largely unaffected supplies from the fifteen fields already under development it would at least slow down plans to invest in the twenty-one fields, a selection from which is listed in Table 6.3. A price reduction would therefore probably reduce supplies of North Sea oil in the 1980s and 1990s below the levels implied by the two higher curves in Figure 3.3. The precise influence of a price decline would depend not only on its size but on its timing; other things being equal, the later the decline the less would be its impact since a greater proportion of North Sea costs would have become unavoidable.

A further effect would most likely come via exploration effort. The highest curve in Figure 3.3, which raises the peak of British North Sea output and prolongs it into the late 1980s, assumes further discoveries of oil. Most likely, however, a moderate price reduction in the next few years would adversely affect exploration effort because of its impact on expected returns from new discoveries (Table 6.4).

TABLE 6.4 The Sensitivity of Project Returns to Price: Assumed Future Discoveries' Real Internal Rates of Return after Tax (percentage)[a]

Field size (million barrels recoverable reserves)[c]	Price scenario[b]		
	CPI	LPD	UMP
100	11	2	20
200	25	17	35
300	20	13	29
400	19	13	28
700	16	11	25

[a] Using the forecasts of the wholesale price index given in Chapter 4, note 4.
[b] See pp. 121–2.
[c] Assumptions about future discoveries and field size groups are explained in Chapter 3.

SOURCE Authors' estimates.

On the other hand, substantial price increases in the future could result in greater North Sea oil supplies than estimated in the surprise-free projection in Chapter 3. Tables 6.2 to 6.4 demonstrate the significant improvement in real rates of return which the UMP scenario is estimated to yield as compared with CPI. The selected fields so far discovered but not yet being developed (Table 6.3) and the assumed future discoveries (Table 6.4) are estimated to give real internal rates of return of at least 20 per cent and in most cases considerably more. Although one cannot be sure what profitability criteria individual companies will apply, or whether their calculations will be similar to those shown here, expected real returns of this order of magnitude would be likely to speed up development, as compared with the production profiles in Figure 3.3; they might well encourage investment to increase rates of recovery from known reserves, and they would almost certainly lead to enhanced exploration efforts compared with the assumptions made in Chapter 3. Up the mid-1980s, the impact on supplies would probably be fairly small. The most likely effect of higher prices than presently expected would be a somewhat increased North Sea output peak (government depletion policy permitting) and a rather longer period before production decline sets in than shown in Figure 3.3.

One final important point needs to be made. Since in this chapter the objective has been to assess the influence of prices on North Sea activity, there is a danger of leaving the impression that high oil prices would be a 'good thing' for Britain as they would improve North Sea profitability and would most probably increase the supply of North Sea oil. However, one can hardly equate the welfare of the British nation with the quantity of North Sea oil which it produces. In particular, one needs to beware of the popular view that some protection for North Sea oil is justified to stop output declining if prices fall. One would war. to examine very carefully the nature and causes of any price reduction and the wider circumstances of the world energy market before concluding that another protective instrument is required in the Birtish energy market. There would, for instance, be a great deal of difference between a price fall deliberately engineered by some or all of the OPEC producers in an attempt to force out of the market competing suppliers and a price fall resulting from a greater abundance of oil in the world. If oil were to become more plentiful – unlikely as this may seem at present – there is no reason why North Sea producers should be protected from the ensuing decline in prices.

'S AND REFERENCES

1. n earlier version of the analysis made in this Chapter appeared as hinson and Morgan, 'World Oil Prices and the Prof bility of North Sea *Petroleum Review*, London, April 1976. See also, Robinson and M. 'The Econo of N th Sea Oil Supplies', *The Chemical Enginee*, London, Jun , and Robinson and Morgan, *North Sea Oil and the British Econom 977–198 (London: d Hall, 1977) pp. 36–40.
2. Fields which employ floating prod and/or tanker loading will have a lower ratio of unavoidao osts at this stage of project life.
3. *Financial Times*, London, 31 January
4. See, for example, *The Oilman*, London,
5. In practice, one also finds that differen within the same company differ in their views about the appro of discount. See also notes 7, 8 and 9 in Chapter 4.
6. Chapter 4 explains that all estimates of future costs and revenues are expressed in terms of unit costs and prices expected to rule in the relevant future periods. By this means, cost and price changes specific to the North Sea are built into the calculations.
7. The real rates of return quoted assume 6 to 8 per cent per annum general

inflation, which is an approximation to the general trend of the forecasts given in note 4, Chapter 4.

8. The papers referred to in reference 1 above use scenarios which are in terms of the price of Light Arabian crude oil.

9. See, for example, *The Petroleum Economist*, London, June 1977, p. 248.

10. For example, the CIA report evidently made to President Carter – see *Financial Times*, 20 April 1977 – and the WAES Report, *Energy – Global Prospects 1985–2000: Workshop on Alternative Energy Strategies* (Maidenhead: McGraw-Hill, 1977).

CHAPTER 7

The Effects of Depletion Control on British North Sea Oil

The Petroleum and Submarine Pipelines Act of 1975 gives the United Kingdom's Secretary of State for Energy very extensive powers to regulate North Sea oil depletion rates if he decides either that it is in the 'national interest' to do so or if he states that there is a 'national emergency'.[1] As pointed out in Chapter 2, there are also other means by which the Government could control North Sea output – for example, by means of the Energy Act of 1976, or by the licence allocation system, or through the operations of the British National Oil Corporation. In the detailed review of depletion policy in Chapter 2 it is argued that although there is a case for a reserve power to allow the government to control production in exceptional circumstances, there is only a very weak theoretical foundation for the kind of detailed regulation which the Petroleum and Submarine Pipelines Act seems to imply.

For example, there is no real basis for the popular view that oil companies, left to themselves, will generally tend to deplete fields at a rate greater than 'the optimum' (which is itself not a very clear concept in this context). Certainly there is no reason to believe that government action will invariably lead to a depletion rate which, from the point of view of the community as a whole, is more desirable than a rate determined by the oil companies. Indeed, as Chapter 6 suggests, producing companies might, under the proposed system of depletion control, lose some of their flexibility to adjust to actual and expected price changes. For example, economic theory would lead one to believe that an expectation of lower prices (net of costs) in the future would cause producers to increase output in the near term, whereas expectations of price increases would, at the margin, tend to make them hold back production. Such desirable reactions would presumably not be possible under strictly applied depletion controls.

Given that the Government has the powers conferred by the Petroleum and Submarine Pipelines Act, the Energy Act and the other instruments mentioned above, this chapter considers what effect the use of such powers might have on the producing companies. One major problem in such an analysis is to guess what use governments may make of the extensive authority they have taken. Up to the end of 1977, although companies were submitting development plans to the Department of Energy in accordance with the Petroleum and Submarine Pipelines Act, the only control imposed by the government appears to have been to reduce gas flaring. For example, in June 1977 Shell and Esso were told to reduce output from the Brent field in order to avoid flaring.[2] The approach employed here is to use the hypothetical field models introduced in Chapter 4 so as to investigate the possible impact of regulations which fall broadly within the so-called 'Varley Guidelines' of December 1974 (the only guide available to the possible extent of controls), and then to conclude with some more qualitative views.[3] The guidelines are set out in Chapter 2 (pages 30–1).

These guidelines seem to have been intended to reassure the oil companies that there would, in practice, be some constraints on the very wide powers to regulate depletion which the Petroleum and Submarine Pipelines Act confers on the Minister. At first sight the guidelines seem fairly explicit but they are much less clear when one considers them in detail. For instance, there is some doubt about the base figure to which the percentage production cut limits apply. It is impossible to know whether future governments will apply depletion controls at equal percentage rates to all fields or whether they will discriminate or hold back new developments to avoid reducing plateau rates of production for established fields. In the analysis which follows one interpretation of the Varley guidelines is provided but it must be emphasised that there is scope for argument about what the guidelines mean. This uncertainty over the form of future depletion controls is an important matter to which further consideration is given in the conclusion to this chapter.

Another qualification which must be made is that the analysis of the effects of depletion control on the producing companies is in terms of profitability – more specifically, the impact on the estimated after tax[4] net present values and internal rates of return of hypothetical North Sea projects. To perform such calculations necessitates making estimates of costs and revenues for twenty years or more into the future. As repeatedly emphasised in earlier chapters, there is great uncertainty surrounding any such figures and this should be borne in mind when considering the rates of return quoted. Moreover, one cannot be sure that the return from a particular project, seen in isolation, is an adequate measure of the total return to a company from undertaking that project. Especially when dealing with multinationals, one would really like to be able to assess the marginal costs and marginal revenues to the company as a whole from North Sea ventures. Finally, the estimates concern the impact *ex post* of production cuts. That is, the figures show what the rates of return will turn out to be, on given assumptions about output, costs, taxes and prices, if cuts of certain sizes or development delays are imposed during a project. A company viewing a project *ex ante*, however, does not know what output reductions, if any, may be made. The prospect of depletion control tends to generate uncertainty – which is not taken into account by the profitability calculations presented here.

THE TEST CASES

From the Varley guidelines four distinct examples can be extracted of depletion control provisions which may be applied to various hypothetical field models. They are as follows:

A. Project begins in 1977; depletion controls apply from 1982 onwards;

B. Project begins in 1980; depletion controls apply from the fourth year of production. Both A and B would be finds made before the end of 1975 under existing licences;

C. Project begins in 1980; depletion controls are imposed after 150 per cent of investment has been recovered. This example would apply to finds made after the end of 1975 under existing licences;

D. Project begins in 1980 but is then subject to development delays. These include a delay of a year in start-up, a further delay of a year in reaching peak production and a reduction in output of about 10 per cent compared with the unrestrained plateau production rate. This example applies to a find made after the end of 1975 under either a new or old licence.

In each example use is made of four of the hypothetical field models explained in Chapter 4 which have recoverable reserves of 200, 300, 400 and 700 million barrels respectively (referred to as the 200, 300, 400 and 700 fields in the rest of this chapter). Model field specifications up to the year 2000, on the assumption of no depletion controls (the Base Case), are detailed in Table 4.3 (Chapter 4). These model fields are necessarily simplifications. In particular, all capital expenditure is assumed to occur in the early years of the project and then falls to zero. In reality, it could spread over a longer period but any likely spreading should not seriously affect the calculations of rates of return. In Tables 7.1 and 7.2 corresponding hypothetical field specifications for projects starting in 1980 (as in Examples B, C and D) are set out. No production cuts are at this stage included in Table 7.1 but Table 7.2 incorporates development delays and output reductions as specified for Example D.

As is explained in Chapter 4 there is still considerable uncertainty about the likely magnitude of operating costs, which is hardly surprising as only a small number of fields has been producing for any significant

TABLE 7.1 Model Field Specifications[a] for Examples B and C

	1980	'81	'82	'83	'84	'85	'86	'87	'88	'89	'90	'91	'92	'93	'94	'95	'96	'97	'98	'99	2000	Total
Production (thousand barrels per day)																						(million barrels)
200				45[b]	60	60	60	52	43	36	31	26	22	18	15	13	11	9	8	6	5	190
300							20[b]	50	50	80	80	67	58	50	44	38	33	29	25	22	19	254
400							10[b]	45	75	100	100	84	75	67	59	53	47	42	37	33	30	313
700							45[b]	70	105	135	150	150	150	150	130	112	97	84	73	63	54	573
Operating costs (£ million)																						(£ million)
200				19	26	27	29	29	29	29	29	29	29	29	29	29	29	29	29	29	29	507
300							14	30	32	32	32	32	32	32	32	32	32	32	32	32	32	460
400							18	37	39	40	40	40	40	40	40	40	40	40	40	40	40	574
700							21	48	70	80	80	80	80	80	80	80	80	80	80	80	80	1099
Capital costs (£ million)																						(£ million)
200	72	123	77	21	8																	301
300	5	11	47	57	117	148	65	31	24	17	18											540
400	5	11	51	65	136	158	67	31	32	34	34											624
700	5	10	139	209	231	182	67	31	148	230	157	34										1443

[a] Field sizes (200, 300, 400, 700) are expressed in million barrels of recoverable reserves.

[b] First year of production: 200 and 700 fields, 9 months; 300 and 400 fields, 6 months; with corresponding reductions in operating costs.

SOURCE Authors' estimates.

TABLE 7.2 Model Field Specifications[a] for Example D

	1980	'81	'82	'83	'84	'85	'86	'87	'88	'89	1990	'91	'92	'93	'94	'95	'96	'97	'98	'99	2000	Total[c]
																						(million barrels)
Production (thousand barrels per day)																						
200	20b					40	54	54	54	52	44	37	31	26	22	18	15	13	11	9	8	185
300								20b	40	60	72	72	72	63	55	48	42	36	31	27	24	242
400								10b	30	60	80	90	90	81	72	64	57	51	45	40	36	294
700								35b	60	80	100	120	135	135	135	135	133	115	99	86	74	526
																						(£ million)
Operating costs (£ million)																						
200					22	30	32	33	33	33	33	33	33	33	33	33	33	33	33	33	33	546
300								25	30	36	38	38	38	38	38	38	38	38	38	38	38	509
400								20	43	44	46	46	46	46	46	46	46	46	46	46	46	613
700								25	55	80	92	92	92	92	92	92	92	92	92	92	92	1172
																						(£ million)
Capital costs (£ million)																						
200	80	136	85	23	9																	333
300	6	12	52	63	129	163	71	34	27	19	20											595
400	6	12	57	72	150	174	73	34	36	38	38											688
700	6	12	138	230	256	200	73	34	163	253	172	37										1573

[a] Field sizes (200, 300, 400, 700) are expressed in million barrels of recoverable reserves.

[b] First year of production: 200 and 700 fields, 9 months; 300 and 400 fields, 6 months; with corresponding reduction in operating costs.

[c] Individual years' values are rounded and so may not add up to totals.

SOURCE Authors' estimates.

length of time and of course the general inflationary prospect is unclear. An estimate is made of average annual operating costs for each of the model fields and this is escalated until three or four years after the start of production using the procedure explained in Chapter 4. Once this point is reached, average annual costs remain fixed in money terms, implying that further increases will tend to be offset by declining insurance charges and a learning curve effect (see Chapter 4). In Examples B and C (Table 7.1), therefore, where the project begins in 1980 rather than in 1977, it is assumed that operating costs start from a higher level than in the Base Case – that is, there is no learning until a field begins to produce. The 300 field, for example, with a 1980 start has average annual operating costs of about £32 million at the plateau rate of output compared with £29 million in the Base Case (Table 4.3).

In all cases the capital cost estimates contain an allowance for future inflation along the lines explained in Chapter 4. For instance, capital expenditure figures for the 300 field in the first year of output are £54 million in the Base Case (for 1983) and £65 million in Examples B and C (for 1986). An allowance for inflation is also included in capital costs for fields from which production has begun. The intention, for both capital and operating costs, is to make estimates in current prices (that is, prices ruling in the year to which the estimate applies), not in real terms. All the DCF returns quoted are therefore in money terms.[5]

In Example D (Table 7.2) the main change from Table 7.1, apart from an assumed delay in commissioning the main platform for the 700 field, arises from the assumption that development delays, if imposed once a decision has been taken to proceed with a project, will mean extra costs. As a consequence capital and operating expenditures have been increased by about 10 per cent for all fields.[6] Whilst start-up and the achievement of peak production are each delayed by one year and the peak is reduced by about 10 per cent for all fields, it is assumed that operators will be allowed to recover the residual reserves without further control and to some extent therefore they will make up 'lost' production.

ANALYSIS OF TEST CASES

Having defined the model fields, the terms of the Varley guidelines, and the four test cases, it is now possible to examine the relative severity of the controls – in terms of their impact on after-tax company returns – using computerised financial analysis programmes that are similar to those described in earlier chapters. The effects of production cuts in the range 10 per cent to 30 per cent per annum (as compared with the output rates shown in Tables 4.3 and 7.1) are examined for Examples A, B and C. The fairly severe assumption is made that once production controls have been imposed they will be maintained at the same level for the remainder of the field's life. In Example D, which illustrates the effect of development delays, it is assumed that no further reduction beyond the 10 per cent cut in the plateau level (already incorporated in Table 7.2) will be imposed.

An important variable in all the calculations is the future price of oil and so use is made of the three price scenarios — Crude Price Indexation, Limited Price Decline and Use of Monopoly Power — explained in Chapter 6. Company returns after tax for the Base Case (no depletion controls) and percentage government 'take' for each project under the three price assumptions are given in Table 7.3. Returns for the 1977 and 1980 project start years are included. In all cases the NPV is calculated at a 20 per cent discount rate as in previous chapters. Values for the 1980 project start are discounted back to 1977 for ease of comparison. Whereas most of the NPVs for a 1980 start are significantly lower than for a 1977 start, Table 7.3 shows that there is little difference between the IRRs for the two start-year cases. Under the Limited Price Decline scenario the larger projects have the same IRR but falling prices in the late 1970s improve NPVs in the 1980 start case.

At the other extreme, sharply rising oil prices more than offset the effects of cost escalation under the Use of Monopoly Power forecast and

TABLE 7.3 Base Case Company Returns[a] after Tax and Government 'Take' under Three Price Scenarios

	Crude Price Indexation			Limited Price Decline			Use of Monopoly Power		
	IRR (%)	NPV[b] £ million	Take[c] (%)	IRR (%)	NPV[b] £ million	Take[c] (%)	IRR (%)	NPV[b] £ million	Take[c] (%)
1977 start									
200	34	105	64	25	32	64	44	217	63
300	27	65	63	20	0	62	37	185	67
400	26	68	66	20	−4	63	35	207	69
700	23	75	67	18	−43	61	32	310	71
1980 start									
200	33	70	63	23	14	63	46	168	63
300	27	46	64	20	1	62	39	144	67
400	26	48	66	20	−3	64	37	156	68
700	24	52	68	18	−29	61	34	239	71

[a] In money (not real) terms.
[b] At a 20 per cent discount rate.
[c] Government share of net revenue (gross revenue less capital and operating costs) consisting of royalties, PRT and corporation tax.

SOURCE Authors' estimates.

all the projects have an improved internal rate of return with a 1980 project start. The price scenarios produce a wide range in expected returns both for the same field size and for the group as a whole: the 200 field's internal rate of return of 23 per cent under the LPD scenario with a 1980 start is, for example, doubled under the UMP assumptions. There is also no clear indication that the larger fields are more profitable, although their NPVs are somewhat more sensitive to changed price assumptions. Of course, the absence of any economies of size effect on project returns simply emphasises the specifications of the various models: the 200 field has an undiscounted unit capital cost which is lower than the 700 field (£1.3 per barrel produced against £1.7). Since all the fields require substantial investment before production can commence, small changes in the capital cost schedule have a considerable influence on the expected rate of return.

Taking the first example of the effect of depletion controls – Example A in Table 7.4 – it appears that the controls do not severely reduce overall returns. Taking the CPI scenario and assuming a 20 per cent cut in output (the maximum under the Varley guidelines), the percentage point reductions in IRR are 3 for the 200 field and 4 for each of the other fields (see Table 7.7). The main explanation for the relative insensitivity of project returns to the production cuts lies in the substantial tax allowances which permit rapid recovery of the heavily 'front-end-loaded' investment. The so-called 'safeguards' available in the Petroleum Revenue Tax (see Chapters 4 and 5) also reduce the impact of depletion controls by automatically permitting reductions in tax liability. But where the PRT liability is cancelled altogether, the percentage government take may actually increase. This effect is illustrated in Figure 7.1 for the CPI scenario. Government take is defined as royalties plus PRT and Corporation Tax as a percentage of net sales revenue (that is gross revenue less operating and capital costs). Since royalties are determined on gross revenues, as net revenues and hence tax liabilities decrease the share of royalties in the government take increases sharply. However, the Government has power to remit royalty payments at ministerial discretion.

Examples B and C are compared in Table 7.5. Cuts are imposed from the fourth year of production for B and after 150 per cent of the investment has been recovered from net cash flow in Example C. Table 7.5 and Table 7.7 show that company returns are generally higher in Example C than in B but that in most cases the difference is small – less than 3 percentage points for a 20 per cent cut. In Example C the Base Case IRR is barely altered, emphasising the way in which the tax structure allows the operators to recoup substantial cash outlay in the first few years of production.

Table 7.6 illustrates the effect of development delays on project returns using the assumptions of Example D. Generally, the impact is

TABLE 7.4 Company Returns after Tax[a] and Government Take
Example A. Depletion Controls from 1982

	Cut (%)	Crude Price Indexation			Limited Price Decline			Use of Monopoly Power		
		IRR (%)	NPV[b] £ million	Take[c] (%)	IRR (%)	NPV[b] £ million	Take[c] (%)	IRR (%)	NPV[b] £ million	Take[c] (%)
200	10	32	90	63	23	21	63	43	196	63
	20	31	73	63	21	8	63	41	175	62
Field	30	29	57	62	19	−6	64	40	153	62
300	10	25	45	62	18	−15	61	35	158	66
	20	23	24	62	16	−32	60	32	130	63
Field	30	20	2	61	14	−53	61	30	100	61
400	10	24	46	64	18	−19	61	33	175	68
	20	22	24	62	16	−39	60	31	143	67
Field	30	20	−1	61	14	−60	60	29	109	65
700	10	22	36	65	16	−79	61	30	251	70
	20	20	−4	63	14	−117	60	28	193	69
Field	30	18	−46	61	12	−162	61	25	130	67

[a] In money (not real) terms.
[b] At a 20 per cent discount rate.
[c] Government share of net revenue (gross revenue less capital and operating costs) consisting of royalties, PRT and corporation tax.

SOURCE Authors' estimates.

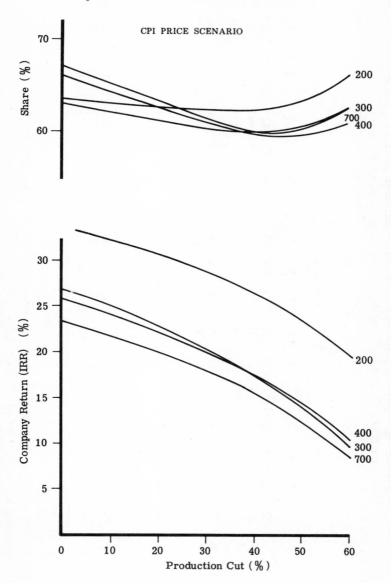

FIG. 7.1 Government Share of Net Revenues and Company Return after Tax against Production Cut (Example A)

SOURCE Authors' estimates.

TABLE 7.5   Company Returns[a] after Tax and Government 'Take'
Examples B and C compared (the 4-year and 150 per cent rules)

		Crude Price Indexation						Limited Price Decline						Use of Monopoly Power					
		IRR (%)		NPV[b] (£ million)		Take[c] (%)		IRR (%)		NPV[b] (£ million)		Take[c] (%)		IRR (%)		NPV[b] (£ million)		Take[c] (%)	
	Cut	B	C	B	C	B	C	B	C	B	C	B	C	B	C	B	C	B	C
200	10	32	32	62	66	62	63	22	23	8	14	63	63	45	45	155	158	62	62
	20	31	32	54	63	62	63	20	23	2	13	63	63	44	44	142	147	62	62
Field	30	29	32	45	59	62	64	19	23	−6	13	63	64	42	44	128	136	61	62
300	10	26	27	39	45	62	63	19	20	−5	0	60	62	38	39	131	136	66	66
	20	25	27	30	42	62	63	18	20	−11	0	59	62	37	38	119	129	64	65
Field	30	24	26	21	39	61	63	17	20	−19	−1	59	63	36	38	107	122	63	64
400	10	25	26	38	45	65	65	19	20	−9	−3	61	63	36	37	140	146	67	68
	20	24	26	28	43	63	65	18	19	−16	−4	59	64	35	36	124	136	66	67
Field	30	22	25	17	40	61	64	16	19	−26	−5	59	65	33	35	108	126	65	66
700	10	22	23	35	51	67	67	17	18	−43	−30	60	62	33	34	210	227	70	70
	20	21	23	20	50	64	67	15	18	−61	−31	59	62	32	33	180	215	69	70
Field	30	20	23	12	50	62	67	14	18	−81	−31	59	63	30	33	150	203	69	69

[a] In money (not real) terms.

[b] At a 20 per cent discount rate.

[c] Government share of net revenue (gross revenue less capital and operating costs) consisting of royalties, PRT and corporation tax.

SOURCE Authors' estimates.

TABLE 7.6 Company Returns[a] after Tax and Government 'Take'
Example D (Development Delays)

	Crude Price Indexation			Limited Price Decline			Use of Monopoly Power		
	IRR *per cent*	NPV[b] *£ million*	Take[c] *per cent*	IRR *per cent*	NPV[b] *£ million*	Take[c] *per cent*	IRR *per cent*	NPV[b] *£ million*	Take[c] *per cent*
200 Field	21	8	62	15	−37	62	30	100	63
300 Field	20	0	63	15	−40	62	29	95	65
400 Field	20	−2	65	15	−47	64	28	91	66
700 Field	17	−50	68	13	−120	62	25	109	69

[a] In money (not real) terms.
[b] At a 20 per cent discount rate
[c] Government share of net revenue (gross revenue less capital and operating costs) consisting of royalties, PRT and corporation tax.

SOURCE Authors' estimates.

substantially greater than in Examples B and C. As Table 7.7 shows, Example D results in a particularly sharp fall in the profitability of the 200 field but returns from the other fields are also significantly worse. In both the LPD and CPI cases the returns (given in money terms) would probably be considered sub-marginal by a producer.[7] One can of course argue with the assumptions used in constructing Example D but it is not an extreme case. In practice costs might rise by less than the 10 per cent assumed here, as companies adapted to the development delays, but the delays themselves could be longer than assumed and the production cut could be greater than the 10 per cent used here.

TABLE 7.7 Reduction in After-tax Internal Rate of Return Compared with the Base Case[a]
Crude Price Indexation Scenario

| | Example | | | | | | | |
| | A | | B | | C | | D | |
	percentage points	per cent	percentage points	per cent	percentage points	per cent	percentage points	per cent
200 Field	3	10	3	10	1	2	12	36
300 Field	4	16	2	8	1	2	7	26
400 Field	4	15	2	9	1	2	6	23
700 Field	4	15	2	9	0	0	7	29

[a] Assuming 20 per cent production cuts for Examples A, B and C.

SOURCE Tables 7.3 to 7.6.

Another way of examining depletion controls is to consider at what level they might cause operators to pull out of established projects. Such a decision would presumably take into account whether the returns offered by the residual after-tax cash flow for a given level of depletion control were acceptable (see Chapter 6). That is, a producer would assess his return on the remainder of a project (ignoring previous unavoidable costs), making some assumptions about depletion control.

As an illustration, a 20 per cent after-tax money DCF return can be used as a cut-off[8] to calculate the extent to which production could be reduced from a particular year of a project onwards and yet still allow this return to be reached from net cash flows from the rest of the project (Figure 7.2). The calculations suggest that by the time a field begins to produce, the 20 per cent return could be achieved – if earlier cash flows are ignored – at production levels of one quarter or less of those planned. Under a regular annual increase in sales price, which is implicit in all the scenarios from about 1980 onwards, the increases in revenue effectively compensate for increasing unit operating costs. Under the CPI forecast a 'plateau' base level of between 10 and 20 per cent of maximum planned production is reached by the end of the first decade of the project's life. Eventually, however, the required production level begins to increase, in some cases quite markedly, as rising price fails to offset larger unit operating costs.

It seems improbable, therefore, that any production cuts likely to be imposed by the Government would affect *fields already producing* so seriously as to cause operators to walk away from their investments. However, as was pointed out in Chapter 6 in the similar analysis of the effects of price reductions, the existence of depletion control would most probably more seriously affect the willingness to develop *fields already discovered* and *exploration activity* where all, or nearly all, costs are avoidable.

CONCLUSIONS

The broad conclusion which emerges from the model field analyses is that, subject to all the qualifications made in this chapter, implemen-

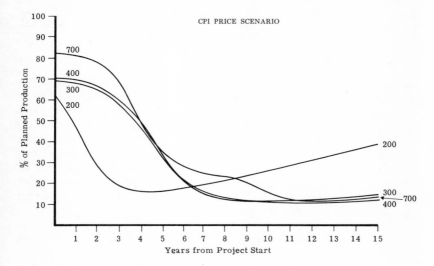

FIG. 7.2(i)   The Production Level (Expressed as a Percentage of Planned Production) at which 20 Per Cent IRR after Tax is Achieved, against Number of Years into Project

SOURCE Authors' estimates.

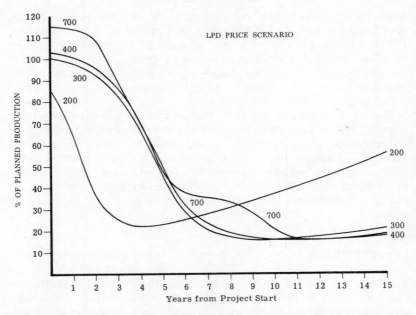

F IG. 7.2(ii)   The Production Level (Expressed as a Percentage of Planned Production) at which 20 Per Cent IRR after Tax is Achieved, against Number of Years into Project

SOURCE Authors' estimates.

tation of production cuts within the Varley guidelines would probably not have severe effects on the profitability of most North Sea fields. Development delays in conjuction with production cuts and possible consequential cost increases (Example D), however, might well have a significantly greater impact on profitability – and therefore, indirectly, on supplies – from new fields with all or most of their costs avoidable. More generally, it is of course true that any North Sea field which, in the absence of regulation, would be expected to earn a return just acceptable to the potential producer might show a negative net present value (at the producer's opportunity cost of capital) under a control regime.

These conclusions are not particularly surprising. On present forecasts of capital and operating costs (see Chapters 4 and 6) many North Sea fields seem likely to be profitable ventures by oil company standards. The analysis here simply shows that production cuts *within the limits of the Varley guidelines* may still leave many fields reasonably profitable (given all the assumptions which have been made about costs, prices and tax rates), but that delaying revenues and raising costs can be expected to hit DCF returns more severely.

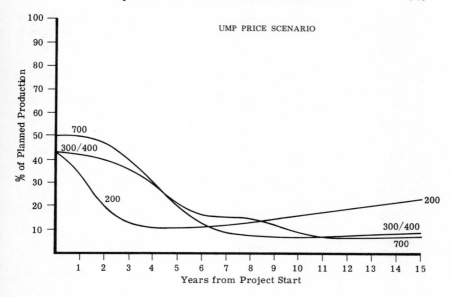

FIG 7.2(iii)   The Production Level (Expressed as a Percentage of Planned Production) at which 20 Per Cent IRR after Tax is Achieved, against Number of Years into Project

SOURCE Authors' estimates.

There are some further qualifications which need to be expressed about the calculations. For example, profitability calculations cannot easily demonstrate the extra uncertainty which depletion controls may generate and which seems to be an inevitable consequence of political involvement in production decisions. As no one can be sure how in practice the Varley guidelines will be operated, there must be some doubt about what allowable production levels will be in the future. More seriously, the companies must wonder for how long the guidelines will last. It has already been pointed out that the Energy Act may not be consistent with the guidelines. Even an Act of Parliament cannot bind succeeding governments – much less a ministerial statement in the House of Commons. So, to uncertainty about what the present guidelines will mean in practice, is added uncertainty about how they might be varied in the future. Then there is the question of the efficiency of North Sea operations. Presumably if companies have to alter production programmes there will be some cost in doing so, as assumed in Example D. Production costs may well be increased and extra management time is likely to be taken up in discussions with the regulatory authority and in coping with the revised programmes. Also, where separate arrangements have been made to produce associated gas or condensate fractions from the field, many further complications can be envisaged.

It is, in fact, quite difficult to isolate and evaluate all the side-effects of depletion control. The analyses presented in this chapter and in Chapter 2 are brought together in Chapter 9 as part of a discussion of government policy towards the North Sea.

NOTES AND REFERENCES

1. A similar analysis, using earlier data, appeared as Morgan and Robinson, 'Depletion Control and Profitability: the Case of the UK North Sea', *Energy Policy*, Guildford, September 1976. See also Robinson and Morgan, 'The Economics of North Sea Oil Supplies', *The Chemical Engineer*, London, June 1977.
2. *Financial Times*, 29 June 1977.
3. *House of Commons, Hansard*, Written Answers, 6 December 1974, cols. 648–50.
4. 'After tax' means (as elsewhere in this book) after royalty, Corporation Tax and Petroleum Revenue Tax. The tax system for offshore oil is described in Chapters 4 and 5.
5. In Chapter 6 real rates of return on the hypothetical fields are quoted. In this chapter the main concern is with the likely *change* in profitability caused by depletion control and so it is not of great significance whether the base returns are in money or real terms.
6. The 10 per cent increase in costs is obviously rather arbitrary. It is used merely in order to indicate the likely *direction* of the effect on costs of development delays. In Morgan and Robinson, 'Depletion Control and Profitability', *op. cit.*, no cost increases are explicitly assumed although it is pointed out that such increases might well occur.
7. That is, a potential producer who foresaw the extent of depletion control would be unlikely to proceed with development of a field at such a prospective rate of return.
8. See Chapter 4, note 7, and Chapter 6, note 5. As explained in Chapter 6, the results of these kinds of calculations are not very sensitive to the DCF return used. Using a 30 per cent cut-off rate in money terms, which is probably a closer approximation to what a producing company would require, would not alter the broad conclusions given here.

CHAPTER 8

Effects of North Sea Oil on Britain's Balance of Payments

As explained in Chapter 1, the first discoveries of oil in the British sector of the North Sea — from 1970 onwards — coincided with the initial show of strength by the less developed oil-producing countries, which achieved a remarkable increase in their 'take' from crude oil between 1970 and 1975.[1] In 1970, the Saudi Arabian Government's revenues were about 90 cents for every barrel of its light crude oil sold, whereas by late 1975 they were over $11. It appeared, therefore, that by remarkable good fortune Britain had struck oil at the right time. Although it would have been preferable for the first discoveries to have been made a few years earlier, so that production could have begun in the early 1970s, when oil prices were already rising, rather than in 1975, nevertheless by 1980 the United Kingdom and Norway seemed likely to become the only substantial oil producers in Western Europe. North Sea oil seemed to offer the prospect of escape from the balance-of-payments constraint which had apparently hampered Britain's economic growth for many years. Whereas her overseas competitors would still have to import expensive OPEC crude oil, Britain would be able to substitute indigenous oil output for the imports she would otherwise have had to make and she might well, eventually, become a net exporter of crude oil.

During 1974, when such euphoric thoughts about the British economy prevailed, a very large balance-of-payments deficit on current account of nearly £3400 million (almost 5 per cent of gross domestic product at factor cost) was financed without difficulty, in spite of rapid inflation, partly because North Sea oil was on the horizon.[2] Gradually, however, in 1975 and 1976, when smaller deficits had to be financed partly by considerable drawings on foreign exchange reserves (notwithstanding a sharp depreciation in sterling) and eventually an International Monetary Fund loan had to be negotiated, awareness dawned that North Sea oil would not necessarily have any significant and lasting favourable effect on the economy: it would directly replace foreign crude oil but it would be no substitute for domestic enterprise and competent economic management.

In this connection, it is instructive to look at the example of Britain's North Sea gas, which has been flowing since late 1968 but appears to have had little effect on economic performance, although it is difficult to know what would have happened in its absence. Natural gas output in 1976 was equivalent to about 34 million tonnes of oil per annum. If one assumes that it substituted for oil which would otherwise have been imported, it should have yielded a visible trade saving of around £1700 million (roughly 1.5 per cent of GDP at factor cost) at 1976 oil prices. It is a sobering thought that such substantial balance-of-payments savings from indigenous natural gas output should have passed almost without notice. Indeed, according to the Department of Energy, the overall (current and long-term capital account) balance-of-payments benefit from North Sea gas in 1976 was over £2000 million.[3]

In this chapter conclusions are drawn about the likely order of magnitude of the balance-of-payments impact of North Sea oil. Some further comments on the more general effects on the British economy are in Chapter 9. At the outset it should be explained that there are serious difficulties in quantifying balance-of-payments and other economic effects which stem largely from uncertainty about what the state of the United Kingdom's economy might have been in the absence of offshore oil. The analysis in this chapter purports to assess the general order of magnitude of the difference in the United Kingdom's balance of payments between two situations: the first in which some stated quantity of North Sea oil is produced and the second with no North Sea oil. It is not an attempt to assess the United Kingdom's future overall balance-of-payments surplus or deficit but to estimate the *difference* which North Sea oil may in the future make. Several sensitivity analyses are performed, in which the production of oil, the world price of oil and other variables are changed, but the standard of comparison is always with a situation of no North Sea oil.

This procedure is quite different from a comparison with pre-North Sea days when the c.i.f. import price of crude oil (in dollars) was less than one quarter of its mid-1977 level. Even though there is considerable doubt about future costs of North Sea exploitation (see Chapter 4), all fields are likely to have costs greater than the c.i.f. import price of crude oil in mid-1973 (about £10 per ton, equivalent to $3.3 per barrel at the then exchange rate of $2.50 = £1). Even the lowest-cost North Sea fields will probably have costs in excess of $3.3 per barrel (at 1973 prices) when a normal rate of return is included. In other words, the resources which the United Kingdom will have to devote to extracting a ton of North Sea crude oil in future will, on average, be greater than the resources used before October 1973 to import a ton of OPEC crude. North Sea oil should, however, bring a potential gain *relative to other countries* as between the two periods: that is, our absolute loss over time from the world oil price increase is likely to be less than the absolute losses of most other countries.

SOME CONCEPTUAL ISSUES

The objective of this chapter is to measure the difference in the United Kingdom's balance of payments as between a future 'North Sea' state (NS) and a future 'no North Sea' state (nNS). For the reasons given above, one has to compare two hypothetical futures rather than relate a hypothetical future to a known past. It is assumed that the effect will be on the *United Kingdom*'s balance of payments, not on the payments of an independent Scotland or Shetland or some other area of what is now the United Kingdom. By the balance of payments is meant the balance on current and long-term capital account; if one assumes that short-term capital movements will not vary between the two states, the balance-of-payments effect as measured here represents the difference in foreign-exchange reserves between NS and nNS.

The principal gain to the British economy from exploiting North Sea oil will accrue, not because the oil is indigenous, but because it allows an improved use of resources. If the resources used in the North Sea would have been otherwise *un*employed, their opportunity cost in North Sea use is zero, which means a clear GNP gain. If they are drawn from alternative uses, then a benefit appears if, as seems probable, the positive price-cost margin in North Sea production exceeds the corresponding margin in the alternative uses. In this paper, the same degree of capacity utilisation is assumed in NS as in nNS since this is convenient analytically, although it may somewhat understate the gain from North Sea oil, for it is quite probable that some of the resources used in the North Sea would otherwise have been unemployed. Essentially, there-fore, the gains calculated here arise from better use of resources. There may also be subsidiary benefits – for example North Sea oil may improve the security of energy supplies and there may even be 'psychic income' to be derived from nationalist delight in owning oil reserves – but the main gain seems likely to accrue from more efficient use of resources.

If, to simplify, one thinks of the initial switch in resources in NS versus nNS as occurring solely within the fuel sector, a GNP gain will arise in NS if the resources devoted to the exploration for and development of offshore oilfields are less than those which would have been required to obtain a comparable quantity of fuel from the lowest-cost alternative (such as imported oil or coal, home-produced coal, or electricity from nuclear fission). *A priori*, one would expect there to be such a surplus of resources in NS, compared with nNS, after satisfying the same energy requirements; real GNP should therefore rise as those resources are, on our assumptions, employed. This real GNP increase represents a *potential*, although not necessarily an actual, balance-of-payments gain. For instance, there might be an increase in home absorption which would remove some or all of the potential improvement in overseas payments. Or, instead of an increase in reserves, there might be an appreciation of sterling in NS versus nNS. Throughout most of the chapter for the sake of brevity the word 'potential' — as applied to the calculations of balance-of-payments gain — is omitted. There is further discussion at the end of the chapter of how much of the potential gain may be realised.

It can be shown that the increase in real GNP, which is equivalent to the balance-of-payments gain, will on certain assumptions also be equal to the government revenue increase in NS versus nNS. [4] If the resources which move into North Sea and associated work (or, more generally, move as a consequence of North Sea exploitation) would otherwise have earned only normal profit, and if they continue to do so because the government captures all rent arising from the change from nNS to NS, then all the GNP gain will simply be channelled into higher government revenue. This, however, is not the same as saying that the GNP gain will be identical to the increase in government revenue provided the government extracts all rent earned by the North Sea producers, because there may well be other sources of rent as a consequence of the North Sea (for instance, suppliers of North Sea equipment and services).

In practice one can only take the difference in government revenue from North Sea producers in NS versus nNS as a very rough indication of the balance-of-payments benefit. Other rents will probably arise from the advent of North Sea oil which will not be taxed away and, in any case, not all rent earned by the North Sea producers is likely to go to the government via royalties, Corporation Tax and Petroleum Revenue Tax. Most probably there will be a significant increase in factor incomes after tax in NS as compared with nNS. [5]

Balance-of-payments effects are therefore estimated by separate examination of the principal components of the trade and capital accounts where there seem likely to be significant changes in NS versus nNS. There are, of course, dangers in looking at individual components of the balance of payments and then aggregating, but an attempt is made to allow for interrelationships among the different sectors. The resulting estimates of the balance-of-payments effect should exceed estimated government tax revenues from the North Sea oil producers for reasons given above. Some comparisons between the payments effect and tax revenues are given in Chapter 9.

One of the main problems is knowing where to stop the analysis since one can conceive of all manner of effects which North Sea oil may have on the structure of the United Kingdom's economy. The procedure used here is to attempt to consider, or at least make assumptions about, those effects which appear directly related to North Sea oil (such as the impact on the oil companies' non-North Sea operations and on equipment and service suppliers), but not less direct effects on the rest of the economy. Ideally, one would like to analyse the full shift of resources in NS compared with nNS and examine its balance-of-payments implications, but such a task seems quite impracticable. Clearly the method employed here is somewhat unsatisfactory. However, given that the objective is to compare an uncertain future NS with an uncertain future nNS so as to assess the general magnitude of change, the most important feature of the analysis is an explicit statement of assumptions and a description of how sensitive are the conclusions to variations in those assumptions.

It is unfortunate that these basic tenets of forecasting, or any kind of assessment of the future, are largely ignored in the only 'official' published works on North Sea oil and the balance of payments: two very brief Treasury articles in the July 1976 and August 1977 issues of *Economic Progress Report.*[6] In these otherwise interesting contributions, the Treasury lapses into various obscurities which seem designed to leave the reader guessing at what precisely has been done. For example, instead of explaining exactly what oil price assumptions have been made, the 1976 article makes such unhelpful statements as (i) that oil prices in future are assumed to rise at the same rate as the prices of world exports of manufactures; (ii) that the latter are assumed to increase 'more slowly than the general level of prices in the earlier years of the period' (1975–85); and (iii) that the general price level in OECD is assumed to rise at 'about the same rate' as 'over the last quarter or two'. The 1977 article is slightly more explicit but it still gives no indication of how sensitive the estimates are to different price and production assumptions.

GENERAL ASSUMPTIONS

The assumptions used in the balance-of-payments analysis fall into two groups. Specific assumptions about particular components of the balance-of-payments effect are explained in the next two sections. More general assumptions which define the framework of analysis of NS versus nNS are given in this section and their consequences are discussed briefly. Some of these general assumptions are little more than expressions of ignorance about future developments; even so, they should be exposed to the reader.

FACTOR EMPLOYMENT

In both NS and nNS the level of employment of productive factors is assumed to be the same so that the balance-of-payments gain arises from more efficient use of factors. As explained earlier, if the advent of North Sea oil were to increase capacity utilisation in the economy, as compared with nNS, there would be an additional potential gain (provided the rate of inflation were not increased in NS versus nNS) which has not been taken into account.

EXCHANGE RATE

Sterling's rate of exchange is assumed to be the same in NS as in nNS. The potential balance-of-payments effect of North Sea oil could be defined either in terms of an exchange-rate appreciation or an improvement in foreign-exchange reserves. Since it is difficult to measure the impact in terms of sterling appreciation, the calculations in this paper are in terms of reserves, for it seems desirable not to confuse the appreciation effect and the reserves effect. In practice, however, as previously pointed out, what is here termed a balance-of-payments improvement would show up under a floating exchange-rate regime wholly or partly as a higher sterling exchange rate in NS versus nNS, the distribution of gains between sterling appreciation and reserves improvement depending on how 'clean' is the float.

OVERSEAS EARNINGS OF BRITISH-BASED OIL COMPANIES

At present, oil companies resident in the United Kingdom (such as British Petroleum and the British part of Royal Dutch–Shell) have substantial profits on their overseas investments, which appear as a credit in the United Kingdom's invisible transactions. The exact sum is concealed in the balance-of-payments accounts,[7] but the item 'other credits (including oil companies)' in the Interest, Profits and Dividends table amounted to £610 million in 1975 and £708 million in 1976. To the extent that such earnings have been derived from oil production overseas, they may diminish in the future (or at least fall relative to output) as the oil-producing countries take control, but there is no real basis for estimating the relative effects of NS versus nNS. The most probable impact is that the advent of North Sea oil production will not so much diminish such output (primarily in the OPEC countries) relative to nNS as slightly reduce the price at which it is sold (see the next section). No attempt is made to quantify this effect on invisible credits: attention is drawn to it as a possible – if rather small – adverse balance-of-payments effect of North Sea oil. Similarly, it is possible that the United Kingdom's tanker earnings will be reduced slightly in NS versus nNS because short-haul oil exports from the country will take the place of long-haul crude-oil imports into the country.

Given the assumption about overseas earnings of oil companies resident in the United Kingdom, it seems reasonable to assume that any reduction in NS versus nNS in their capital outflow to finance overseas operations (£240 million in 1975 and £391 million in 1976, including miscellaneous non-oil transactions) will be small enough to disregard, given that concern is with the general order of magnitude of the balance-of-payments effect.

EARNINGS OF OVERSEAS OIL COMPANIES OPERATING IN BRITAIN

Such earnings have generally been rather small and in some years negative. In 1975 they were £7 million and in 1976, −£46 million. Assumptions specific to the North Sea operations of overseas oil companies are described below. It is assumed that profits on their other United Kingdom operations (that is, refining, marketing and distribution) do not differ between NS and nNS. That is, the substitution of North Sea for imported oil is assumed to leave the United Kingdom's oil consumption about the same and not significantly to affect the profitability of the companies' United Kingdom activities except by creating profits on oil production. In practice, it is possible that in the long term the oil industry in Britain will adapt to the presence of an indigenous oil supply — so that there is a difference between NS and nNS — but no adjustment has been made for any such effect.

CAPITAL INFLOW FROM OVERSEAS COMPANIES OPERATING IN BRITAIN

To be consistent, it is assumed that capital inflow from overseas oil companies to finance non-North Sea oil activities in the United Kingdom is the same in NS and nNS. Before North Sea oil development began, the inflow was of the order of £200 million to £300 million per annum. The capital inflow on account of North Sea oil operations is estimated as described on pages 179–80.

PRICE ASSUMPTIONS

Oil price assumptions are crucial in this kind of analysis and it is extremely important to be explicit and to demonstrate the sensitivity of one's conclusions to varying price assumptions. As elsewhere in this book, North Sea oil producers are assumed to be price-takers in the world oil market (see Chapters 1 and 6). They accept the world market price for crude oil and the price of North Sea oil diverges from the world price only on account of differentials for quality and location.

The three price scenarios explained in Chapter 6 and set out in Table 6.1 are used to analyse balance-of-payments effects. Briefly, the scenarios represent three possible states of the future world oil market — continuously rising prices (CPI), a moderate decline to 1980 and then increasing prices (LPD) and a case in which OPEC uses its power to engineer further sharp price increases (UMP).

An awkward problem which arises in the balance-of-payments analysis, however, is whether one should assume that world prices would be different in NS from nNS. In principle, prices would be expected to be somewhat lower in NS since, although they believe themselves to be price-takers, North Sea producers collectively are increasing the world supply of oil, thus shifting the world oil supply curve to the right, tending to reduce price and increase quantity consumed. The relative sizes of the price and quantity effects would be a function of the elasticity of demand.

The procedure adopted here in estimating the visible trade effect of North Sea oil, is to value North Sea output in a given year at the North Sea price for that year derived from a given scenario. The scenarios, however, in principle take into account the North Sea effect on prices, so if no adjustment is made for that effect there is a slight inconsistency. In estimating the oil visible trade difference between NS and nNS one ought really to take the nNS price (the price at which imports would have been made *in the absence of the North Sea*) which would be higher. No adjustment has been made for this minor inconsistency because of another roughly offsetting price factor: the United Kingdom might well have imported crude oil of lower quality than the North Sea average had there been no North Sea, at a slightly lower price. Two other possible adjustments which could have been made, but which do not appear worth while (given that the aim is only to assess the general magnitude of the balance-of-payments effect) are as follows. First, one could differentiate between the import substitution and export prices of North Sea crude oil. From the beginning some North Sea crude is being exported and in the 1980s there may well be substantial net exports. The exporter would normally receive a little less than the c.i.f. import price used here because of transport costs to the point of consumption. Second, the analysis here is all in terms of *crude* oil flows and related prices: it does not attempt directly to assess the impact on oil *product* trade and prices.

OUTPUT ASSUMPTIONS

Another critical variable in calculating the effect of North Sea oil on the balance of payments is, of course, oil production. As explained at many points in this book, there is considerable uncertainty about future oil production from the North Sea. For the purpose of estimating balance-of-payments effects and their sensitivity to output variations, the calculations which follow use the three production schedules explained in Chapter 3 and shown in Figure 3.3.These schedules cover a wide range of oil output, from the early 1980s onwards, but they are not intended to span all likely future levels of production from the British offshore area. The surprise-free projections of Chapter 3 are specifically for the British sector of the North Sea between 55° 50' and 62° North. Actual future rates of output will depend *inter alia* on a number of variables discussed in earlier chapters, such as world oil prices (Chapter 6), government depletion controls, if any (Chapters 2 and 7), the tax regime (Chapters 4 and 5) and cost movements (Chapter 4). As explained in Chapter 3 it is also possible that significant oil discoveries will be made in the areas to the west of Britain, which are not considered here.

THE CALCULATIONS IN GENERAL

Before describing the detailed calculations it is worth reiterating that the objective is to estimate the balance-of-payments difference, NS *minus* nNS. Statements that items are 'positive' or 'credits' therefore mean that they improve NS relative to nNS; 'negative' or 'debit' items improve nNS compared with NS.

All the detailed calculations are based on the estimates described earlier in the book of recoverable oil reserves, depletion rates, capital expenditure programmes and operating costs. A series of computer programs which, as explained in Chapter 4, incorporates the United Kingdom's tax system for offshore oil is used to analyse production, price and cost statistics in order to estimate company cash flows and government tax revenues field by field and year by year. Each field is assessed individually and the relevant results are abstracted and aggregated in another program which calculates the balance of payments effects for a specified group of fields. There are considerable differences in estimated costs among North Sea fields and the complexities of the tax system (especially the effects of the 'safeguard clauses' in Petroleum Revenue Tax) mean that the only satisfactory way to estimate corporate cash flows and government revenue is by considering each field and each year separately.

Corporation Tax at the present rate has been calculated separately for each field, since each company's tax position is not known; this may result in some misjudgement of the actual timing of tax payments (see Chapter 5), but not of the amounts eventually paid. Estimates of Petroleum Revenue Tax assume that the present rate of 45 per cent and the present allowances remain. Royalties are calculated as explained in Chapters 4 and 5.

All the tax calculations are made in sterling to avoid distortions of tax-allowable losses because of variations in the exchange rate. Details of the field characteristics assumed and the cost estimates (in current prices) used are given in Chapters 3 and 4. When interpreting the results it is extremely important to bear in mind that very little oil has yet been produced from the North Sea so that cost forecasts many years ahead can only indicate general orders of magnitude. The estimates of reserves and depletion rates are also subject to substantial errors. The calculations which are shown in Tables 8.1 to 8.9 are therefore only to be regarded as very approximate indicators based on present ideas about prices, costs, reserves and depletion rates.

Nine estimates of the balance-of-payments impact of North Sea oil are given in Tables 8.1 to 8.9: each table combines one of the three price scenarios (CPI, LPD, UMP) with one of the three estimates of North Sea oil production (for established commercial fields, for established commercial and potentially commercial fields, and for all fields including assumed future discoveries).[8] All the calculations are in current prices – not in real terms. Totals are not always equal to the sum of their components because of rounding.

VISIBLE TRADE EFFECTS

VISIBLE OIL TRADE

The dominant credit item in each table is the value of crude oil production, which is an approximate measure of the direct effect of North Sea oil as it will appear in the balance of trade statistics. It is dominant because of the substantial margin between the world price of oil and the costs of extracting oil from the North Sea. This relatively high margin, compared with other possible investments, is the main source of gain from North Sea oil. In NS, as compared with nNS, resources move into producing offshore oil, thus reducing the oil imports which would have been made in nNS and probably generating net oil exports in the 1980s. Each table shows the volume of North Sea oil production, varying according to the assumption made about development and exploration activity. The value of oil production is computed by multiplying by North Sea oil prices taken from the relevant price scenario (Table 6.1). No attempt is made to differentiate between the import substitution and export generation effects of North Sea oil production.

The size of the visible oil trade effect arising from North Sea oil is, of course, sensitive to variations in both oil output and oil prices. For instance, taking the CPI price scenario so as to hold the price effect constant, Tables 8.1 to 8.3 demonstrate that the estimated oil trade effect varies with production as follows:

Visible oil trade effect (£'000 million rounded): CPI Scenario

Production from

	Established Commercial Fields (Table 8.1)	Established and Potentially Commercial Fields (Table 8.2)	All Fields (Table 8.3)
1980	7	8	8
1985	6	13	14
1990	4	10	15

In 1980 the estimated effects are virtually indentical because output then is almost entirely from fields already shown to be commercially attractive, but in 1985 and still more so in 1990 there are big differences in the visible trade effects depending on what one assumes about development of the potentially commercial fields and about future exploration successes.

Price sensitivity can be illustrated by selecting a production case and varying the price scenario. Using the all-fields production case (Tables 8.3, 8.6 and 8.9) the estimated oil trade effect varies with price as follows:

Visible oil trade effect (£'000 million rounded): all fields

Price scenario

	CPI (Table 8.3)	LPD (Table 8.6)	UMP (Table 8.9)
1980	8	6	10
1985	14	10	20
1990	15	10	25

There is quite a substantial variation even in 1980 because of the price differences assumed for that year. In 1985 and 1990 changes in price assumptions make big differences to the estimated visible trade effect.

This analysis of the visible oil trade effect brings out something which is often left unclear in the more simplified published investigations of the effect of North Sea oil on overseas payments – that there is great sensitivity to price and output assumptions. In 1985, for example, the tables show a very wide range for the visible oil trade balance of £4300 million (Table 8.4) to £20,300 million (Table 8.9). The apparent implication of these estimates – that the United Kingdom balance of payments gains more and more the higher oil prices rise – should be viewed with caution because the 'gains' are all by reference to nNS. They may merely indicate that nNS would have been a very difficult state. British consumers stand to lose directly from higher oil prices, although once Britain becomes a significant oil exporter there will be a terms-of-trade benefit from high oil prices to the extent that they do not cause other import prices to be increased.

TABLES 8.1–9   ESTIMATED IMPACT OF NORTH SEA OIL ON THE UNITED KINGDOM BALANCE OF PAYMENTS (NS MINUS nNS)

TABLE 8.1   Crude Price Indexation Price Scenario with Production from Established Commercial Fields

Year	North Sea Oil Production	Current Account							Capital Account		Current and Long-term Capital Balance
		Visible Trade				Invisibles					
		Value of Oil Production	Imports of North Sea Goods and Services	Exports of Oil Equipment etc. and Factor Switching	Visible Trade Balance	Interest Abroad	Profits Abroad	Current Account Balance	Capital Inflows	Capital Outflows	
	(million tonnes)							(million sterling at current prices)			
1975	01	0.1	−0.6	0.1	−0.4	−0.0	0.0	−0.5	0.7	0.0	0.2
1976	12	0.7	−1.0	0.1	−0.2	−0.1	0.0	−0.3	1.2	−0.2	0.7
1977	40	2.6	−1.0	0.2	1.7	−0.2	−0.2	1.3	1.2	−0.3	2.3
1978	69	4.6	−0.8	0.2	4.0	−0.3	−0.9	2.8	0.9	−0.6	3.2
1979	88	6.2	−0.6	0.2	5.8	−0.3	−1.0	4.5	0.6	−1.1	4.0
1980	100	7.4	−0.4	0.2	7.2	−0.3	−0.8	6.1	0.3	−1.7	4.6

1981	101	7.8	−0.3	0.2	7.7	−0.1	−1.7	5.9	0.1	−0.6	5.4
1982	97	7.9	−0.3	0.2	7.9	−0.1	−0.9	6.9	0.0	−0.4	6.5
1983	87	7.5	−0.2	0.2	7.4	−0.0	−1.1	6.3	0.0	−0.2	6.2
1984	74	6.6	−0.2	0.2	6.6	0.0	−0.9	5.8	0.0	0.0	5.8
1985	64	6.1	−0.2	0.2	6.1	0.0	−0.8	5.3	0.0	0.0	5.3
1986	56	5.7	−0.2	0.2	5.7	0.0	−0.9	4.8	0.0	0.0	4.8
1987	49	5.3	−0.2	0.2	5.3	0.0	−0.8	4.5	0.0	0.0	4.5
1988	43	5.0	−0.2	0.2	5.0	0.0	−0.8	4.2	0.0	0.0	4.2
1989	38	4.7	−0.2	0.2	4.7	0.0	−0.7	4.0	0.0	0.0	4.0
1990	33	4.3	−0.2	0.2	4.3	0.0	−0.7	3.7	0.0	0.0	3.7
1991	29	4.0	−0.2	0.2	4.0	0.0	−0.6	3.4	0.0	0.0	3.4
1992	25	3.8	−0.2	0.2	3.8	0.0	−0.6	3.2	0.0	0.0	3.2
1993	21	3.4	−0.2	0.2	3.4	0.0	−0.5	2.9	0.0	0.0	2.9
1994	18	3.2	−0.2	0.2	3.2	0.0	−0.5	2.7	0.0	0.0	2.7
1995	13	2.5	−0.1	0.1	2.5	0.0	−0.4	2.1	0.0	0.0	2.1
1996	12	2.3	−0.1	0.1	2.3	0.0	−0.4	1.9	0.0	0.0	1.9
1997	10	2.1	−0.1	0.1	2.1	0.0	−0.4	1.7	0.0	0.0	1.7
1998	07	1.6	−0.1	0.1	1.6	0.0	−0.2	1.4	0.0	0.0	1.4
1999	06	1.5	−0.1	0.1	1.5	0.0	−0.3	1.2	0.0	0.0	1.2
2000	06	1.5	−0.1	0.1	1.5	0.0	−0.3	1.2	0.0	0.0	1.2
Total	1099	108.5	−8.2	4.6	104.9	−1.3	−16.5	87.0	4.9	−5.1	86.9

SOURCE Authors' estimates.

TABLE 8.2   Crude Price Indexation Price Scenario with Production from Established Commercial and Potentially Commercial Fields

		Current Account							Capital Account		Current and Long-term Capital Balance
		Visible Trade				Invisibles					
Year	North Sea Oil Production	Value of Oil Production	Imports of North Sea Goods and Services	Exports of Oil Equipment etc. and Factor Switching	Visible Trade Balance	Interest Abroad	Profits Abroad	Current Account Balance	Capital Inflows	Capital Outflows	
	(million tonnes)					(million sterling at current prices)					
1975	01	0.1	−0.6	0.1	−0.4	−0.0	0.0	−0.5	0.7	0.0	0.2
1976	12	0.7	−1.0	0.1	−0.2	−0.1	0.0	−0.3	1.2	−0.2	0.7
1977	40	2.6	−1.1	0.2	1.6	−0.2	−0.2	1.3	1.4	−0.3	2.4
1978	69	4.6	−1.0	0.2	3.8	−0.3	−0.8	2.7	1.3	−0.6	3.4
1979	89	6.3	−0.9	0.3	5.6	−0.3	−1.0	4.3	1.2	−1.1	4.4
1980	103	7.6	−0.9	0.3	7.1	−0.3	−0.8	6.0	1.3	−1.8	5.4
1981	109	8.5	−1.0	0.4	7.8	−0.2	−1.9	5.8	1.5	−0.6	6.7

Year											
1982	118	9.6	−0.9	0.4	9.1	−0.4	−0.9	7.8	1.3	−1.0	8.1
1983	132	11.3	−0.7	0.5	11.1	−0.5	−1.4	9.1	0.8	−1.7	8.2
1984	137	12.3	−0.6	0.5	12.3	−0.5	−1.8	10.0	0.4	−2.1	8.4
1985	136	12.9	−0.6	0.6	12.9	−0.3	−2.2	10.4	0.3	−1.8	8.9
1986	127	12.8	−0.5	0.5	12.8	−0.1	−2.3	10.3	0.1	−0.8	9.6
1987	114	12.3	−0.4	0.4	12.3	−0.1	−2.0	10.3	0.0	−0.5	9.8
1988	100	11.6	−0.4	0.4	11.6	−0.0	−2.2	9.4	0.0	−0.0	9.4
1989	86	10.6	−0.4	0.4	10.6	0.0	−1.7	8.9	0.0	0.0	8.9
1990	73	9.7	−0.4	0.4	9.7	0.0	−1.8	8.0	0.0	0.0	8.0
1991	62	8.7	−0.4	0.4	8.7	0.0	−1.5	7.2	0.0	0.0	7.2
1992	53	8.0	−0.4	0.4	8.0	0.0	−1.5	6.5	0.0	0.0	6.5
1993	45	7.3	−0.4	0.4	7.3	0.0	−1.4	5.9	0.0	0.0	5.9
1994	38	6.6	−0.3	0.3	6.6	0.0	−1.3	5.3	0.0	0.0	5.3
1995	30	5.5	−0.3	0.3	5.5	0.0	−1.1	4.5	0.0	0.0	4.5
1996	26	5.1	−0.3	0.3	5.1	0.0	−1.0	4.2	0.0	0.0	4.2
1997	22	4.6	−0.3	0.3	4.6	0.0	−1.0	3.7	0.0	0.0	3.7
1998	16	3.7	−0.2	0.2	3.7	0.0	−0.6	3.1	0.0	0.0	3.1
1999	14	3.3	−0.2	0.2	3.3	0.0	−0.7	2.7	0.0	0.0	2.7
2000	10	2.6	−0.2	0.2	2.6	0.0	−0.4	2.1	0.0	0.0	2.1
Total	1762	189.0	−14.4	8.6	183.2	−3.4	−31.4	148.5	11.6	−12.6	147.5

SOURCE Authors' estimates.

TABLE 8.3   Crude Price Indexation Price Scenario with Production from All Fields

	North Sea Oil Production	Value of Oil Production	Current Account						Capital Account		Current and Long-term Capital Balance
			Visible Trade			Invisibles					
Year			Imports of North Sea Goods and Services	Exports of Oil Equipment etc. and Factor Switching	Visible Trade Balance	Interest Abroad	Profits Abroad	Current Account Balance	Capital Inflows	Capital Outflows	
	(million tonnes)										
					(million sterling at current prices)						
1975	01	0.1	−0.6	0.1	−0.4	−0.0	0.0	−0.5	0.7	0.0	0.2
1976	12	0.7	−1.0	0.1	−0.2	−0.1	0.0	−0.3	1.2	−0.2	0.7
1977	40	2.6	−1.1	0.2	1.7	−0.2	−0.2	1.3	1.4	−0.3	2.4
1978	69	4.6	−1.0	0.3	3.9	−0.3	−0.8	2.8	1.3	−0.6	3.5
1979	89	6.3	−0.9	0.4	5.8	−0.3	−1.0	4.4	1.2	−1.1	4.5
1980	103	7.6	−1.0	0.5	7.2	−0.3	−0.8	6.1	1.3	−1.8	5.6
1981	109	8.5	−1.1	0.6	7.9	−0.2	−1.8	5.9	1.7	−0.6	7.0
1982	118	9.6	−1.2	0.7	9.1	−0.4	−0.9	7.8	1.8	−1.0	8.6

1983	132	11.3	−1.2	0.8	10.9	−0.5	−1.3	9.0	1.6	−1.7	8.9
1984	142	12.8	−1.1	0.9	12.6	−0.6	−1.7	10.4	1.2	−2.3	9.3
1985	150	14.1	−1.0	1.0	14.1	−0.4	−2.2	11.5	0.9	−2.4	10.0
1986	154	15.6	−0.8	0.8	15.6	−0.4	−2.5	12.7	0.4	−1.8	11.3
1987	148	16.0	−0.7	0.7	16.0	−0.2	−2.3	13.4	0.3	−1.5	12.2
1988	140	16.2	−0.9	0.9	16.2	−0.1	−2.5	13.5	0.5	−0.7	13.4
1989	125	15.5	−1.0	1.0	15.5	−0.1	−2.0	13.4	0.7	−0.5	13.6
1990	112	14.8	−1.0	1.0	14.8	−0.1	−2.1	12.7	0.7	−0.2	13.2
1991	102	14.4	−1.0	1.0	14.4	−0.2	−1.8	12.5	0.7	−0.6	12.6
1992	94	14.2	−1.0	1.0	14.2	−0.2	−1.8	12.3	0.6	−0.8	12.0
1993	89	14.4	−1.1	1.1	14.4	−0.1	−1.9	12.3	0.7	−0.8	12.2
1994	82	14.3	−1.3	1.3	14.3	−0.1	−1.7	12.5	1.0	−1.0	12.4
1995	72	13.4	−1.3	1.3	13.4	−0.1	−1.6	11.7	1.1	−0.5	12.3
1996	70	13.9	−1.3	1.3	13.9	−0.3	−1.4	12.2	1.0	−0.8	12.4
1997	67	14.2	−1.4	1.4	14.2	−0.3	−1.4	12.4	1.1	−1.4	12.1
1998	61	14.0	−1.5	1.5	14.0	−0.3	−1.2	12.5	1.2	−1.4	12.4
1999	58	14.2	−1.7	1.7	14.2	−0.2	−1.3	12.6	1.5	−1.1	13.0
2000	53	13.9	−1.7	1.7	13.9	−0.2	−1.0	12.7	1.5	−1.2	13.0
Total	2392	297.1	−29.2	23.6	291.5	−6.3	−37.3	248.0	27.2	−26.4	248.8

SOURCE Authors' estimates.

TABLE 8.4   Limited Price Decline Price Scenario with Production from Established Commercial Fields

Year	North Sea Oil Production (million tonnes)	Value of Oil Production	Imports of North Sea Goods and Services	Exports of Oil Equipment etc. and Factor Switching	Visible Trade Balance	Interest Abroad	Profits Abroad	Current Account Balance	Capital Inflows	Capital Outflows	Current and Long-term Capital Balance
			Visible Trade			*Invisibles*			*Capital Account*		
						(million sterling at current prices)					
1975	01	0.1	−0.6	0.1	−0.4	−0.0	0.0	−0.5	0.7	0.0	0.2
1976	12	0.7	−1.0	0.1	−0.2	−0.1	0.0	−0.3	1.2	−0.2	0.7
1977	40	2.6	−1.0	0.2	1.7	−0.2	−0.2	1.3	1.2	−0.3	2.3
1978	69	4.2	−0.8	0.2	3.6	−0.3	−0.7	2.6	0.9	−0.5	3.0
1979	88	5.3	−0.6	0.2	4.8	−0.3	−0.8	3.8	0.6	−0.9	3.5
1980	100	5.7	−0.4	0.2	5.5	−0.3	−0.6	4.6	0.3	−1.3	3.6
1981	101	5.9	−0.3	0.2	5.8	−0.2	−0.8	4.9	0.2	−1.1	3.9
1982	97	5.9	−0.3	0.2	5.8	−0.1	−1.1	4.6	0.0	−0.3	4.3

Year											
1983	87	5.5	−0.2	0.2	5.4	−0.0	−0.5	4.9	0.0	−0.4	4.6
1984	74	4.8	−0.2	0.2	4.8	−0.0	−0.7	4.0	0.0	−0.0	4.0
1985	64	4.3	−0.2	0.2	4.3	0.0	−0.7	3.6	0.0	0.0	3.6
1986	56	4.0	−0.2	0.2	4.0	0.0	−0.7	3.3	0.0	0.0	3.3
1987	49	3.7	−0.2	0.2	3.7	0.0	−0.6	3.1	0.0	0.0	3.1
1988	43	3.5	−0.2	0.2	3.5	0.0	−0.6	2.9	0.0	0.0	2.9
1989	38	3.3	−0.2	0.2	3.3	0.0	−0.6	2.7	0.0	0.0	2.7
1990	33	3.0	−0.2	0.2	3.0	0.0	−0.5	2.5	0.0	0.0	2.5
1991	29	2.8	−0.2	0.2	2.8	0.0	−0.5	2.3	0.0	0.0	2.3
1992	25	2.6	−0.2	0.2	2.6	0.0	−0.5	2.2	0.0	0.0	2.2
1993	21	2.4	−0.2	0.2	2.4	0.0	−0.4	2.0	0.0	0.0	2.0
1994	18	2.2	−0.2	0.2	2.2	0.0	−0.4	1.8	0.0	0.0	1.8
1995	13	1.7	−0.1	0.1	1.7	0.0	−0.3	1.5	0.0	0.0	1.5
1996	12	1.6	−0.1	0.1	1.6	0.0	−0.3	1.3	0.0	0.0	1.3
1997	10	1.5	−0.1	0.1	1.5	0.0	−0.2	1.2	0.0	0.0	1.2
1998	07	1.1	−0.1	0.1	1.1	0.0	−0.2	1.0	0.0	0.0	1.0
1999	06	1.1	−0.1	0.1	1.1	0.0	−0.2	0.9	0.0	0.0	0.9
2000	06	1.0	−0.1	0.1	1.0	0.0	−0.2	0.8	0.0	0.0	0.8
Total	1099	80.6	−8.2	4.6	77.0	−1.5	−12.2	63.3	5.0	−5.1	63.2

SOURCE Authors' estimates.

TABLE 8.5   Limited Price Decline Price Scenario with Production from Established Commercial and Potentially Commercial Fields

| | | Current Account | | | | | | | | Capital Account | | |
| | North Sea Oil Production | Visible Trade | | | | Invisibles | | | | | | |
Year		Value of Oil Production	Imports of North Sea Goods and Services	Exports of Oil Equipment etc. and Factor Switching	Visible Trade Balance	Interest Abroad	Profits Abroad	Current Account Balance	Capital Inflows	Capital Outflows	Current and Long-term Capital Balance
	(million tonnes)					(million sterling at current prices)					
1975	01	0.1	-0.6	0.1	-0.4	-0.0	0.0	-0.5	0.7	0.0	0.2
1976	12	0.7	-1.0	0.1	-0.2	-0.1	0.0	-0.3	1.2	-0.2	0.7
1977	40	2.6	-1.1	0.2	1.6	-0.2	-0.2	1.3	1.4	-0.3	2.4
1978	69	4.2	-1.0	0.2	3.5	-0.3	-0.7	2.5	1.3	-0.5	3.2
1979	89	5.3	-0.9	0.3	4.7	-0.3	-0.7	3.6	1.2	-0.9	3.9
1980	103	5.9	-0.9	0.3	5.3	-0.3	-0.5	4.5	1.3	-1.4	4.3
1981	109	6.4	-1.0	0.4	5.8	-0.3	-0.8	4.7	1.6	-1.2	5.1

Year											
1982	118	7.2	-0.9	0.4	6.7	-0.4	-1.1	5.1	1.3	-0.7	5.8
1983	132	8.3	-0.7	0.5	8.0	-0.6	-0.6	6.8	0.8	-1.5	6.1
1984	137	8.9	-0.6	0.5	8.8	-0.6	-1.1	7.1	0.5	-1.7	5.9
1985	136	9.1	-0.6	0.6	9.1	-0.4	-1.4	7.2	0.4	-1.8	5.8
1986	127	9.0	-0.5	0.5	9.0	-0.3	-1.5	7.2	0.2	-1.3	6.1
1987	114	8.6	-0.4	0.4	8.6	-0.1	-1.4	7.1	0.0	-0.8	6.3
1988	100	8.1	-0.4	0.4	8.1	-0.1	-1.3	6.7	0.0	-0.4	6.3
1989	86	7.4	-0.4	0.4	7.4	-0.0	-1.3	6.1	0.0	-0.2	6.0
1990	73	6.8	-0.4	0.4	6.8	0.0	-1.3	5.5	0.0	0.0	5.5
1991	62	6.1	-0.4	0.4	6.1	0.0	-1.1	5.0	0.0	0.0	5.0
1992	53	5.6	-0.4	0.4	5.6	0.0	-1.1	4.5	0.0	0.0	4.5
1993	45	5.1	-0.4	0.4	5.1	0.0	-1.0	4.1	0.0	0.0	4.1
1994	38	4.6	-0.3	0.3	4.6	0.0	-0.9	3.7	0.0	0.0	3.7
1995	30	3.9	-0.3	0.3	3.9	0.0	-0.7	3.1	0.0	0.0	3.1
1996	26	3.6	-0.3	0.3	3.6	0.0	-0.7	2.9	0.0	0.0	2.9
1997	22	3.3	-0.3	0.3	3.3	0.0	-0.6	2.6	0.0	0.0	2.6
1998	16	2.6	-0.2	0.2	2.6	0.0	-0.4	2.2	0.0	0.0	2.2
1999	14	2.3	-0.2	0.2	2.3	0.0	-0.4	1.9	0.0	0.0	1.9
2000	10	1.8	-0.2	0.2	1.8	0.0	-0.3	1.5	0.0	0.0	1.5
Total	1762	137.4	-14.4	8.6	131.7	-4.0	-21.4	106.3	11.9	-12.9	105.2

SOURCE Authors' estimates.

TABLE 8.6 Limited Price Decline Price Scenario with Production from All Fields

		Current Account							Capital Account		
		Visible Trade				Invisibles					Current and Long-term Capital Balance
Year	North Sea Oil Production	Value of Oil Production	Imports of North Sea Goods and Services	Exports of Oil Equipment etc. and Factor Switching	Visible Trade Balance	Interest Abroad	Profits Abroad	Current Account Balance	Capital Inflows	Capital Outflows	
	(million tonnes)					(million sterling at current prices)					
1975	01	0.1	−0.6	0.1	−0.4	−0.0	0.0	−0.5	0.7	0.0	0.2
1976	12	0.7	−1.0	0.1	−0.2	−0.1	0.0	−0.3	1.2	−0.2	0.7
1977	40	2.6	−1.1	0.2	1.7	−0.2	−0.2	1.3	1.4	−0.3	2.4
1978	69	4.2	−1.0	0.3	3.6	−0.3	−0.7	2.6	1.3	−0.5	3.3
1979	89	5.3	−0.9	0.4	4.8	−0.3	−0.7	3.7	1.2	−0.9	4.0
1980	103	5.9	−1.0	0.5	5.5	−0.3	−0.5	4.6	1.3	−1.4	4.5
1981	109	6.4	−1.1	0.6	5.9	−0.3	−0.8	4.8	1.8	−1.2	5.5
1982	118	7.2	−1.2	0.7	6.7	−0.4	−1.1	5.2	1.8	−0.7	6.3

1983	132	8.3	−1.2	0.8	7.8	−0.6	−0.5	6.8	1.6	−1.5	6.8
1984	142	9.2	−1.1	0.9	9.0	−0.6	−1.0	7.3	1.2	−1.8	6.8
1985	150	9.9	−1.0	1.0	9.9	−0.6	−1.3	8.0	0.9	−2.2	6.7
1986	154	10.9	−0.8	0.8	10.9	−0.6	−1.5	8.8	0.5	−2.1	7.3
1987	148	11.2	−0.7	0.7	11.2	−0.4	−1.5	9.3	0.3	−1.8	7.9
1988	140	11.3	−0.9	0.9	11.3	−0.2	−1.6	9.6	0.5	−1.2	8.9
1989	125	10.9	−1.0	1.0	10.9	−0.1	−1.5	9.2	0.7	−0.6	9.4
1990	112	10.4	−1.0	1.0	10.4	−0.2	−1.5	8.8	0.7	−0.4	9.1
1991	102	10.1	−1.0	1.0	10.1	−0.2	−1.2	8.7	0.7	−0.8	8.6
1992	94	10.0	−1.0	1.0	10.0	−0.2	−1.3	8.4	0.6	−0.7	8.3
1993	89	10.1	−1.1	1.1	10.1	−0.2	−1.2	8.6	0.7	−0.8	8.6
1994	82	10.0	−1.3	1.3	10.0	−0.2	−1.2	8.7	1.0	−0.9	8.8
1995	72	9.4	−1.3	1.3	9.4	−0.2	−1.0	8.3	1.1	−0.8	8.6
1996	70	9.7	−1.3	1.3	9.7	−0.3	−1.1	8.4	1.0	−0.6	8.8
1997	67	9.9	−1.4	1.4	9.9	−0.3	−0.9	8.7	1.1	−1.1	8.7
1998	61	9.8	−1.5	1.5	9.8	−0.3	−0.6	8.8	1.2	−1.3	8.7
1999	58	9.9	−1.7	1.7	9.9	−0.3	−0.7	8.9	1.5	−1.2	9.2
2000	53	9.7	−1.7	1.7	9.7	−0.3	−0.6	8.9	1.5	−1.1	9.2
Total	2392	213.2	−29.2	23.6	207.6	−7.8	−24.2	175.6	27.6	−25.9	177.3

SOURCE Authors' estimates.

TABLE 8.7 Use of Monopoly Power Price Scenario with Production from Established Commercial Fields

Year	North Sea Oil Production (million tonnes)	Value of Oil Production	Current Account						Capital Account		Current and Long-term Capital Balance
			Visible Trade			Invisibles					
			Imports of North Sea Goods and Services	Exports of Oil Equipment etc. and Factor Switching	Visible Trade Balance	Interest Abroad	Profits Abroad	Current Account Balance	Capital Inflows	Capital Outflows	
							(million sterling at current prices)				
1975	01	0.1	−0.6	0.1	−0.4	−0.0	0.0	−0.5	0.7	0.0	0.2
1976	12	0.7	−1.0	0.1	−0.2	−0.1	0.0	−0.3	1.2	−0.2	0.7
1977	40	2.6	−1.0	0.2	1.7	−0.2	−0.2	1.3	1.2	−0.3	2.3
1978	69	5.5	−0.8	0.2	4.8	−0.3	−1.1	3.5	0.9	−0.7	3.6
1979	88	7.8	−0.6	0.2	7.3	−0.3	−1.4	5.7	0.6	−1.4	4.9
1980	100	9.7	−0.4	0.2	9.5	−0.2	−1.5	7.7	0.3	−1.5	6.4
1981	101	10.4	−0.3	0.2	10.3	−0.1	−2.0	8.2	0.0	−0.4	7.9
1982	97	10.7	−0.3	0.2	10.7	−0.0	−1.4	9.2	0.0	−0.4	8.8

1983	87	10.3	−0.2	0.2	10.3	0.0	−1.7	8.5	0.0	0.0	8.5
1984	74	9.4	−0.2	0.2	9.3	0.0	−1.1	8.2	0.0	0.0	8.2
1985	64	8.7	−0.2	0.2	8.7	0.0	−1.3	7.4	0.0	0.0	7.4
1986	56	9.5	−0.2	0.2	9.5	0.0	−1.9	7.7	0.0	0.0	7.7
1987	49	9.0	−0.2	0.2	9.0	0.0	−1.3	7.6	0.0	0.0	7.6
1988	43	8.4	−0.2	0.2	8.4	0.0	−1.3	7.1	0.0	0.0	7.1
1989	38	7.8	−0.2	0.2	7.8	0.0	−1.2	6.7	0.0	0.0	6.7
1990	33	7.3	−0.2	0.2	7.3	0.0	−1.0	6.3	0.0	0.0	6.3
1991	29	6.8	−0.2	0.2	6.8	0.0	−0.9	5.9	0.0	0.0	5.9
1992	25	6.3	−0.2	0.2	6.3	0.0	−0.9	5.4	0.0	0.0	5.4
1993	21	5.7	−0.2	0.2	5.7	0.0	−0.7	5.1	0.0	0.0	5.1
1994	18	5.4	−0.1	0.1	5.4	0.0	−0.7	4.7	0.0	0.0	4.7
1995	13	4.1	−0.1	0.1	4.1	0.0	−0.5	3.6	0.0	0.0	3.6
1996	12	3.9	−0.1	0.1	3.9	0.0	−0.6	3.3	0.0	0.0	3.3
1997	10	3.5	−0.1	0.1	3.5	0.0	−0.5	3.0	0.0	0.0	3.0
1998	07	2.7	−0.1	0.1	2.7	0.0	−0.3	2.4	0.0	0.0	2.4
1999	06	2.6	−0.1	0.1	2.6	0.0	−0.4	2.2	0.0	0.0	2.2
2000	06	2.5	−0.1	0.1	2.5	0.0	−0.4	2.1	0.0	0.0	2.1
Total	1099	161.3	−8.2	4.6	157.6	−1.2	−24.3	132.1	4.9	−5.0	131.9

SOURCE Authors' estimates.

TABLE 8.8   Use of Monopoly Power Price Scenario with Production from Established Commercial and Potentially Commercial Fields

Year	North Sea Oil Production (million tonnes)	Value of Oil Production	Visible Trade		Visible Trade Balance	Invisibles		Current Account Balance	Capital Account		Current and Long-term Capital Balance
			Imports of North Sea Goods and Services	Exports of Oil Equipment etc. and Factor Switching		Interest Abroad	Profits Abroad		Capital Inflows	Capital Outflows	
						(million sterling at current prices)					
1975	01	0.1	−0.6	0.1	−0.4	−0.0	0.0	−0.5	0.7	0.0	0.2
1976	12	0.7	−1.0	0.1	−0.2	−0.1	0.0	−0.3	1.2	−0.2	0.7
1977	40	2.6	−1.1	0.2	1.6	−0.2	−0.2	1.3	1.4	−0.3	2.4
1978	69	5.5	−1.0	0.2	4.7	−0.3	−1.1	3.4	1.3	−0.7	3.9
1979	89	7.8	−0.9	0.3	7.2	−0.3	−1.3	5.5	1.2	−1.4	5.3
1980	103	10.0	−0.9	0.3	9.4	−0.3	−1.5	7.6	1.3	−1.6	7.2
1981	109	11.3	−1.0	0.4	10.6	−0.2	−2.1	8.3	1.5	−0.5	9.3

Year											
1982	118	13.1	-0.9	0.4	12.6	-0.4	-1.7	10.5	1.3	-1.2	10.6
1983	132	15.6	-0.7	0.5	15.4	-0.5	-2.5	12.4	0.8	-1.9	11.3
1984	137	17.4	-0.6	0.5	17.3	-0.4	-2.9	13.9	0.4	-2.2	12.2
1985	136	18.5	-0.6	0.6	18.5	-0.2	-3.6	14.7	0.2	-1.4	13.4
1986	127	21.5	-0.5	0.5	21.5	-0.1	-4.7	16.7	0.1	-0.7	16.1
1987	114	20.7	-0.4	0.4	20.7	-0.0	-3.8	16.8	0.0	-0.0	16.8
1988	100	19.5	-0.4	0.4	19.5	0.0	-3.4	16.0	0.0	0.0	16.0
1989	86	17.8	-0.4	0.4	17.8	0.0	-3.0	14.8	0.0	0.0	14.8
1990	73	16.3	-0.4	0.4	16.3	0.0	-2.8	13.4	0.0	0.0	13.4
1991	62	14.6	-0.4	0.4	14.6	0.0	-2.4	12.2	0.0	0.0	12.2
1992	53	13.4	-0.4	0.4	13.4	0.0	-2.5	10.9	0.0	0.0	10.9
1993	45	12.2	-0.4	0.4	12.2	0.0	-2.2	10.0	0.0	0.0	10.0
1994	38	11.1	-0.3	0.3	11.1	0.0	-2.0	9.2	0.0	0.0	9.2
1995	30	9.3	-0.3	0.3	9.3	0.0	-1.4	7.9	0.0	0.0	7.9
1996	26	8.6	-0.3	0.3	8.6	0.0	-1.2	7.4	0.0	0.0	7.4
1997	22	7.8	-0.3	0.3	7.8	0.0	-1.2	6.5	0.0	0.0	6.5
1998	16	6.2	-0.2	0.2	6.2	0.0	-0.7	5.4	0.0	0.0	5.4
1999	14	5.5	-0.2	0.2	5.5	0.0	-0.8	4.7	0.0	0.0	4.7
2000	10	4.3	-0.2	0.2	4.3	0.0	-0.6	3.7	0.0	0.0	3.7
Total	1762	291.0	-14.4	8.6	285.3	-2.9	-49.7	232.6	11.3	-12.3	231.6

SOURCE Authors' estimates.

TABLE 8.9 Use of Monopoly Power Price Scenario with Production from All Fields

			Current Account						Capital Account		
			Visible Trade			Invisibles					Current and Long-term Capital Balance
Year	North Sea Oil Production	Value of Oil Production	Imports of North Sea Goods and Services	Exports of Oil Equipment etc. and Factor Switching	Visible Trade Balance	Interest Abroad	Profits Abroad	Current Account Balance	Capital Inflows	Capital Outflows	
	(million tonnes)						(million sterling at current prices)				
1975	01	0.1	−0.6	0.1	−0.4	−0.0	0.0	−0.5	0.7	0.0	0.2
1976	12	0.7	−1.0	0.1	−0.2	−0.1	0.0	−0.3	1.2	−0.2	0.7
1977	40	2.6	−1.1	0.2	1.7	−0.2	−0.2	1.3	1.4	−0.3	2.4
1978	69	5.5	−1.0	0.3	4.8	−0.3	−1.1	3.4	1.3	−0.7	4.0
1979	89	7.8	−0.9	0.4	7.3	−0.3	−1.3	5.6	1.2	−1.4	5.4
1980	103	10.0	−1.0	0.5	9.5	−0.3	−1.5	7.7	1.3	−1.6	7.4
1981	109	11.3	−1.1	0.6	10.7	−0.2	−2.1	8.4	1.7	−0.5	9.6
1982	118	13.1	−1.2	0.7	12.5	−0.4	−1.6	10.5	1.8	−1.2	11.1

Year											
1983	132	15.6	−1.2	0.8	15.2	−0.5	−2.3	12.4	1.6	−1.9	12.0
1984	142	18.0	−1.1	0.9	17.8	−0.5	−2.9	14.5	1.2	−2.5	13.1
1985	150	20.3	−1.0	1.0	20.3	−0.3	−3.7	16.2	0.7	−2.1	14.8
1986	154	26.1	−0.8	0.8	26.1	−0.3	−5.1	20.7	0.4	−2.1	18.9
1987	148	26.8	−0.7	0.7	26.8	−0.1	−4.5	22.2	0.3	−0.9	21.6
1988	140	27.1	−0.9	0.9	27.1	−0.1	−4.1	23.0	0.5	−0.5	23.0
1989	125	26.0	−1.0	1.0	26.0	−0.0	−3.6	22.4	0.6	−0.0	22.9
1990	112	24.8	−1.0	1.0	24.8	−0.1	−3.3	21.4	0.6	−0.2	21.9
1991	102	24.2	−1.0	1.0	24.2	−0.1	−2.9	21.1	0.7	−1.1	20.7
1992	94	23.8	−1.0	1.0	23.8	−0.1	−3.4	20.3	0.6	−0.4	20.5
1993	89	24.1	−1.1	1.1	24.1	−0.2	−2.9	21.1	0.7	−1.2	20.6
1994	82	24.0	−1.3	1.3	24.0	−0.1	−3.0	20.9	1.0	−0.6	21.2
1995	72	22.5	−1.3	1.3	22.5	−0.1	−2.3	20.1	1.1	−0.4	20.7
1996	70	23.3	−1.3	1.3	23.3	−0.2	−2.1	21.0	1.0	−1.3	20.7
1997	67	23.8	−1.4	1.4	23.8	−0.2	−2.4	21.2	1.1	−1.5	20.7
1998	61	23.4	−1.5	1.5	23.4	−0.2	−2.1	21.1	1.2	−1.1	21.3
1999	58	23.8	−1.7	1.7	23.8	−0.2	−1.9	21.7	1.5	−1.1	22.0
2000	53	23.3	−1.7	1.7	23.3	−0.2	−1.8	21.3	1.5	−1.2	21.6
Total	2392	471.9	−29.2	23.6	466.3	−5.0	−62.3	398.9	26.6	−26.3	399.2

SOURCE Authors' estimates.

TRADE EFFECTS FROM NON-OIL TRANSACTIONS

In addition to the direct effect on oil trade, there will be other changes in visible and invisible trade as a consequence of the switch of resources into the North Sea. One of the most obvious effects is that the resources moving into North Sea exploration and production have an import content – for example, production platforms and pipe manufactured abroad and the hire of specialist services from overseas. The import of such goods and services was one of the first balance-of-payments consequences of North Sea oil since it took time for the British supply industry to become established. In 1975 and 1976 these imports were the principal current account balance of payments debit associated with North Sea oil, exceeding the value of oil output.

To forecast this item one can use information from the trade press. In many cases, however, there is little information about likely future imports and some broad assumptions have to be made. It is assumed here that the proportion of imports in total spending on North Sea goods and services, which fell in 1975 and 1976, will continue to decline substantially in the next few years.[9] Because of uncertainty about this item, two alternative assumptions for the future were tested – that the import components of both capital expenditure and operating costs will fall from about 70 per cent in 1974 to 40 per cent in 1981 or to 30 per cent in 1981. Thereafter the percentages are assumed to remain constant in each case. The import component percentages are applied to the estimates of annual capital and operating costs. As the difference between the 30 per cent and 40 per cent import cases turned out to be rather small (about £400 million in 1980) in relation to the aggregate balance-of-payments effect of North Sea oil, only the rather more plausible 40 per cent case is used in Tables 8.1 to 8.9.

According to the estimates in Tables 8.1 to 8.9, imports of goods and services for North Sea work will, from 1977 onwards, be fairly small in relation to the value of oil production. In the 'all fields' production case (Tables 8.3, 8.6 and 8.9), such imports are around £1000 million per annum from now until the mid-1990s, when they rise to some £1500 million a year. In the production cases which exclude any further discoveries but include development of 21 potentially commercial fields (Tables 8.2, 8.5 and 8.8), imports for North Sea work are, of course, lower: they decline to approximately £500 million per annum in the mid-1980s/early 1990s. The third production assumption – development only of established commercial fields – yields a steady decline from 1977 onwards in imports for North Sea work so that in the early 1980s such imports are only around £250 million a year (Tables 8.1, 8.4 and 8.7).

It is quite probable that eventually there will be a substantial offsetting credit item in the form of exports of oil equipment, materials and services from the British offshore supply industry. There are already signs of such export markets appearing but it is premature to attempt any estimate of their size beyond saying that the order of magnitude for the 1980s is probably a few hundreds of millions of pounds. It is assumed that exports of equipment and supplies will be higher the greater is production from the British North Sea — although this is arguable, since it is possible that low North Sea output might stimulate a search for overseas markets by the North Sea suppliers.

The third item to be considered under the heading of non-oil trade transactions is very elusive. Given that the same level of factor employment is assumed in NS and nNS, the switch of resources in NS must mean that there are less resources in other employments. The factors of production which are employed in North Sea-related activities in NS would in nNS have been employed elsewhere and would have attracted imports and generated exports. Consequently in estimating the difference between NS and nNS one ought to try to allow for the loss of imports (a credit in the calculations) and exports (a debit) which would have taken place in nNS. Unfortunately it is very hard to see any real basis for determining what such net imports or net exports would have been in nNS since one does not know where the factors would have been employed.[10]

In other words, the fundamental problem of assessing the balance-of-payments effect of North Sea oil appears — that it is extremely difficult to guess at what the economy would have looked like without the North Sea. Calculations of this factor-switching effect are made in the brief Treasury papers mentioned earlier,[11] where it is assumed that net imports displaced by the North Sea will rise from £500 million in 1976 to £700 million in 1980 and to £1000 million in 1985 (all at 1976 prices). How these estimates are made is not explained, so it would be unwise to use them.

Any estimates of future exports of oil equipment and supplies and of the factor-switching effect must inevitably be highly speculative but at least the assumptions used can be made explicit. In tables 8.1 to 8.9 it is assumed that the factor-switching effect results in the displacement of net *imports* which would have occurred in nNS; the assumed credit on account of factor-switching is added to the assumed exports of oil equipment and supplies to produce a single column in the tables. In all the production cases, the aggregate credit rises steadily until it is assumed to converge by 1985 on the value of imports of goods and services for North Sea work. That is, by 1985 imports of goods and services for North Sea activities are assumed to be precisely offset by the combined credit from exports of oil equipment and supplies and from factor-switching. The assumptions used are obviously rather heroic but they produce a result which, as far as one can judge at this stage of development of the North Sea, appears reasonable. In effect, they lead to the conclusion that from about 1980 onwards — by which time the early surge of equipment and service imports should be over and equipment and service exports should be significant –there should be little difference between the value of oil production and the direct visible trade effect of North Sea oil. It must be pointed out once more, however, that the *indirect* impact of North Sea oil on the British economy may lead to all manner of effects on visible trade which at present cannot be foreseen.

INVISIBLE TRADE EFFECTS

Finally, in considering the current account, there is a negative impact on the invisibles account. In NS, as compared with nNS, there is interest on North Sea loans, and profits after tax and depreciation on North Sea activities which accrue to overseas residents. The interest and profits are assumed to be additional to any such invisible payments which would have occurred in nNS, just as it is assumed that the capital inflow to which they relate is additional to the capital inflow in nNS. Annual interest and profit payments are estimated from the individual field cash flows.

In estimating interest payments all overseas companies are assumed to use a 'North Sea' operating subsidiary which is charged interest on the funds which it receives from the parent. Such interest payments are allowable against Corporation Tax (although not against Petroleum Revenue Tax) provided they are attributable to loans for use within the North Sea 'ring fence'. These operating subsidiaries are assumed to obtain all their finance from abroad. Companies resident in the United Kingdom are assumed to raise abroad half the capital they need for North Sea projects. The rate of interest used is 10 per cent per annum on all loan balances outstanding; although there might be some fall in interest rates if there is a decline in the rate of inflation, the calculations are not very sensitive to variations of 1 or 2 per cent. It is assumed that North Sea loans are repaid from depreciation so that no profits are remitted until the project is fully depreciated. To the extent that a 'production payment' system (in which loan repayments vary with output) is used instead, interest payments in the early years would be lower than stated and profits would be greater. If some overseas companies use straight equity finance, this would reduce interest payments throughout compared with the calculation shown but increase profits.

Profits are treated in the same way as in the United Kingdom's balance-of-payments statistics. All after-tax profits on North Sea activities earned by non-residents of the United Kingdom (calculated from each field's profits in proportion to the overseas share of the licence holding) are included as an invisible outflow, whether actually remitted or not. [12] For assumed future discoveries a 25 per cent overseas interest is used, corresponding to the British National Oil Corporation's 51 per cent share of future licences (or in some cases the British Gas Corporation's share) and a roughly fifty-fifty split of the remainder.

The results suggest that interest payments are, in all price-production cases, a rather minor debit item. In no case do they significantly exceed £500 million in any year, though they rise up to the mid-1980s on the higher production assumptions. Profits accruing to overseas residents are a larger item, although still quite small relative to the visible trade effect. By the early to mid-1980s, depending on the price-production case, profits tend to exceed imports of North Sea equipment and supplies and by the late 1980s they are much greater except in the LPD/all fields case (Table 8.6) where profitability is relatively low but existing fields are being developed and new fields are discovered, thus generating imports. Table 8.6 apart, overseas profits are by far the biggest current balance of payments debit from North Sea oil by the mid to late 1980s. They are, of course, highest in the UMP/all fields case (Table 8.9) at around £3000 million to £5000 million per annum in the late 1980s and early 1990s: even so, they are never equivalent to more than about one fifth of the estimated visible trade effect of North Sea oil in those years.

LONG-TERM CAPITAL-ACCOUNT EFFECTS

In the early years of North Sea oil development there was a considerable inflow of long-term capital from abroad — probably about £1000 million net in 1976. Comparing NS with nNS, one can anticipate that for some years there will be a net positive effect as capital flows in from overseas companies and from financial institutions abroad. For consistency with United Kingdom's balance-of-payments statistics, all North Sea capital expenditure by overseas companies is treated as capital inflow (see note 12). Calculations of capital expenditure by overseas companies are obtained from estimates of capital expenditure field by field and year by year (see Chapter 4) multiplied by the estimated overseas share of each field's recoverable reserves. All such expenditure is treated as an interest-bearing loan. There may also be some inflow of capital to finance activities in the United Kingdom of overseas companies supplying goods and services for the North Sea and possibly other capital movements as an indirect consequence of North Sea oil; none of these has been taken into account.

The estimates of capital inflows (including loans from overseas) and capital outflows (including repayment of overseas loans) in Tables 8.1 to 8.9 suggest that the net capital inflow of the 1970s is likely to turn into a net outflow within a few years. On the higher production cases (that is, excluding Tables 8.1, 8.4 and 8.7) the net outflow rises to about £1000 to £2000 million by the mid-1980s (somewhat less than the rate of outflow of profits abroad at that time), but then declines rapidly to about zero. In the low production cases, the net outflows occur in the late 1970s and early 1980s and the net capital balance then falls to zero. Capital flows are, of course, extremely sensitive to the assumptions made about exploration and development activity: if there were to be another surge in offshore activity in the North Sea proper or in other United Kingdom areas, there would be a further capital inflow with a subsequent outflow.

OVERALL CURRENT AND LONG-TERM CAPITAL-ACCOUNT EFFECTS

As mentioned earlier, the value of oil production is the dominant item in the balance-of-payments impact of North Sea oil (NS minus nNS), according to the assumptions used in this chapter, although there may well be other indirect effects of North Sea oil on the balance of payments which cannot be foreseen. Given the dominance of the credit from the value of oil production and given the sensitivity of that item and several others to the price/production assumptions it follows that the overall balance-of-payments effect (current and long-term capital account) varies considerably with output and price.

The range of estimates for the overall balance-of-payments effect is as follows:

£'000 million (rounded)

	Lowest (Table 8.4)	Highest (Table 8.9)
1980	4	7
1985	4	15
1990	3	22

These very wide ranges can be compressed somewhat by selecting the more plausible cases. For instance, the three cases (Tables 8.1, 8.4 and 8.7) where only the established commercial fields are produced seem to have only low probabilities of occurrence. The high production case for the limited-price-decline scenario (Table 8.6) also seems to have a relatively low probability of occurrence, as do the no-further-discoveries cases for the CPI (Table 8.2) and UMP (Table 8.8) price scenarios. It is not suggested that the probabilities are near-zero for any of these cases — if they were, the cases would not have been included in this chapter — but simply that the more probable cases are those in Tables 8.3, 8.5 and 8.9. In Tables 8.3 and 8.9, oil prices keep on rising, all presently known fields are developed and more discoveries are made: in Table 8.5, prices decline moderately in the near future, exploration activity is curtailed and only presently known fields are exploited. As emphasised at various points in this book, it is not possible to construct a supply curve with respect to price for North Sea oil at this early stage of development, but the three cases selected above seem to have a reasonable degree of consistency between the production and the price assumptions.

A plausible range of estimates for the overall balance of payments effect then becomes:

£'000 million (rounded)

	Lowest (Table 8.5)	*Highest (Table 8.9)*
1980	4	7
1985	6	15
1990	6	22

Estimates beyond 1990 are obviously extremely speculative and are included in the tables only for the sake of comprehensiveness since there is some interest in other calculations of North Sea variables (for example, output) up to the year 2000.

The range of estimates shown above is still rather wide beyond 1980 and will not be to the taste of those who like to see apparently precise-point estimates of future events. Unfortunately, however, the only certain characteristic of the future is uncertainty, and the future effect of North Sea oil on the balance of payments is particularly cloudy. One of the purposes of assessments of future states should be to bring out their inherent uncertainty and to attempt to estimate reasonably likely limits within which future values may lie.[13] It is important to realise that the future impact of North Sea oil on the balance of payments may vary substantially with factors largely outside the United Kingdom's control, such as the geology of the Continental Shelf and the actions of OPEC.

To express the calculations in terms which are perhaps more meaningful – as rough percentages of likely GNP (in current prices) – the 1980 range is 2 to 4 per cent, in 1985 2 to 6 per cent, and in 1990 1 to 6 per cent. All of the benefits are, of course, *by reference to a future state without North Sea oil.*

THE INTEREST-RATE EFFECT

Since the calculations earlier in the chapter show that there is a positive difference between NS and nNS in all future years considered, there is an implication for the United Kingdom's foreign exchange reserves and overseas borrowing. If it is assumed that the whole of the NS balance-of-payments gain will be realised and translated into higher reserves or lower borrowing than would have been the case in nNS, then it appears reasonable to take account of higher interest receipts on cumulative reserves and lower interest payments on cumulative borrowings in NS versus nNS. Such an item for 'interest on extra reserves' is included in the Treasury papers on the balance-of-payments impact of North Sea oil[14] and builds up to the very large sum of £4300 million in 1985 — about 30 per cent of its estimated oil trade effect in that year. No explanation is given of the rate of interest used in making these calculations.

In the next few years it is indeed likely that the United Kingdom will derive some benefit from borrowing less abroad and from extra interest-earning reserves than would have been the case without North Sea oil. To capture this effect, Table 8.10 shows the results of calculations which accumulate, from 1975 onwards, the overall current and capital account benefits stated in Tables 8.3, 8.5 and 8.9 (the most plausible cases, discussed above) and apply an interest rate to these gains. Because of uncertainties about future interest rates, a range of 4 per cent to 8 per cent[15] is used to illustrate the sensitivity of the calculations to interest-rate variations. Up to 1980 the effect is fairly small, but by 1985 the estimated interest rate effect becomes very substantial relative to the previously calculated current and long-term capital effects at £1700 million to £6500 million. Calculations beyond 1985 soon yield annual interest rate effects of huge proportions.

The gain from extra reserves/lower borrowing should, however, be

TABLE 8.10 Estimated Interest Earned on Extra Reserves or Saved on
Reduced Borrowing
(NS minus nNS)

	£'000 million					
	Table 8.3 cases[a]		*Table 8.5 cases[a]*		*Table 8.9 cases[a]*	
	4%	8%	4%	8%	4%	8%
1975	0	0	0	0	0	0
1976	0	0	0	0	0	0
1977	0	0.1	0	0.1	0	0.1
1978	0.1	0.3	0.1	0.3	0.1	0.3
1979	0.3	0.6	0.3	0.5	0.3	0.6
1980	0.5	1.0	0.4	0.9	0.5	1.1
1981	0.7	1.5	0.6	1.3	0.8	1.8
1982	1.0	2.2	0.9	1.8	1.3	2.7
1983	1.4	3.1	1.1	2.4	1.8	3.8
1984	1.8	4.0	1.4	3.1	2.3	5.1
1985	2.3	5.1	1.7	3.9	2.9	6.5

[a] The production and price assumptions are as stated in the table to which reference is made.

SOURCE Authors' estimates.

treated with great caution. As already explained, the calculations in this chapter concern *potential* balance-of-payments gains. In the event, some of the potential benefits to the United Kingdom economy may not appear in the balance of payments; indeed, some of the benefits may not be realised at all. Consequently, one must have misgivings about adding interest on those apparent gains to balance-of-payments gains which may not be realised: it seems more sensible to treat the interest-rate effect separately as a possible bonus on top of the potential gains considered earlier. The wider issue of the effect of North Sea oil on the British economy is pursued in Chapter 9.

NOTES AND REFERENCES

1. Earlier estimates by the authors of the balance-of-payments effects of North Sea oil are in Robinson and Morgan, *Effects of North Sea Oil on the United Kingdom Balance of Payments*, Guest Paper No. 5 (London: Trade Policy Research Centre, November 1976), and Robinson and Morgan, *North Sea Oil and the British Economy, 1977–1985* (London: Staniland Hall, 1977), Part 2.

2. The principal elements in financing were public-sector borrowing of over £1000 million and an increase in the sterling holdings of oil-exporting countries of more than £2200 million.

3. See *Development of the Oil and Gas Resources of the United Kingdom* (London: H.M. Stationery Office, for the Department of Energy, 1977).

4. This point about the equivalence of the GNP, govenment revenue and balance-of-payments gains is made in P. M. Oppenheimer, 'Employment, Balance of Payments and Oil in the U.K.', *Three Banks Review*, London, March 1976, which provides a very useful framework for analysing the payments impact of North Sea oil.

5. The intention here is not to argue the case for or against taxation designed to capture rent from specified sectors of the economy. To avoid misunderstanding, it should nevertheless be pointed out that it is extremely difficult to measure rent, particularly in a new production area where costs are uncertain, there are problems in designing taxes which will cover widely differing field characteristics, the theoretical basis for extracting rent in one sector but not in others is weak, and there are obvious questions of equity. One may also have reservations about the uses which government will make of the revenues. Chapters 4 and 5 analyse in detail the North Sea taxation system.

6. 'The North Sea and the Balance of Payments', *Economic Progress Report* (London: H.M. Stationery Office, July 1976) and 'The North Sea and the UK Economy', *Economic Progress Report* (London: H.M. Stationery Office, August 1977).

7. References to the balance-of-payments accounts are to *United Kingdom Balance of Payments, 1966–76* (London: H.M. Stationery Office, 1977). See also 'Interest, Profits and Dividends in the Balance of Payments', *Economic Trends* (London: H.M. Stationery Office, June 1977).

8. No specific assumptions are made at this stage about the elasticity of supply with respect to price nor about the impact of varying supplies on prices. For discussion of such issues see Chapters 1 and 6 and Robinson and Morgan, 'World Oil Prices and the Profitability of North Sea Oil', *Petroleum Review*, London, April 1976.

9. The import content of *orders placed* for (not expenditure on) North Sea work in 1974, 1975 and 1976 is given in the Department of Energy's Offshore Supplies Report, *Offshore 1976* (London: H.M. Stationery Office, 1977). The United Kingdom's share of orders rose from 40 per cent in 1974 to 52 per cent in 1975 and 57 per cent in 1976.

10. It is quite probable that some of the factors, particularly those specific to Scotland, would not have been employed in nNS.

11. 'The North Sea and the Balance of Payments', and 'The North Sea and the UK Economy', *loc. cit.*

12. For consistency one must then treat all capital committed to the North Sea by overseas companies as an inflow, even if it is from profits retained in this country.

13. See Robinson, *Business Forecasting – An Economic Approach* (London: Nelson, 1971), especially chs 1 and 9.

14. 'The North Sea and the Balance of Payments' and 'The North Sea and the UK Economy', *loc. cit.*

15. In *Economic Progress Report*, (London: H.M. Treasury, May 1977) there is an article about foreign currency borrowing which gives the interest rate on drawings from IMF credit tranches as $4\frac{3}{8}$ to $6\frac{3}{8}$ per cent and on drawings from the IMF oil facility as $7\frac{3}{8}$ to $7\frac{7}{8}$ per cent.

CHAPTER 9

The North Sea, Government Policy and the British Economy

Earlier chapters of this book concentrated on positive analysis. Essentially, they set out the results of an extensive effort by the authors to collect data on North Sea oilfields, to analyse that data by devising computer programs which conform to the particular needs of the North Sea, to review and draw out implications from the relevant legislation, and to put Britain's offshore oil into an international context. The intention is both to make progress in the applications of economic methodology in a research field where some knowledge of the technology is essential and to reveal some of the future possibilities. Although in certain places it is inevitable that one moves away from positive assessment to normative statements – as, for example, in discussing the probable impact of depletion control – the principal aim of preceding chapters is to draw logical conclusions from specified assumptions which seem appropriate at this stage of development of Britain's offshore area. The analysis is deliberately explicit since it is the authors' belief that, given that no one can foresee the future with any precision, those who make 'forecasts' have a responsibility to explain clearly their assumptions and methods so that others can substitute such other assumptions as they prefer. The large number of sensitivity tests in the book may not appeal to those who like to see a view of the future which is clear-cut (and, therefore, almost inevitably incorrect) but the estimates made here are still a gross simplification of a very complex reality.

It is now time to draw some more general conclusions from the research explained in earlier chapters. This chapter begins with a summary of the North Sea supply outlook and the variables to which future output is likely to be most sensitive; it then turns to the controversial issue of government policy towards North Sea oil; and it concludes with some comments on the effects of offshore oil on the British economy.

FUTURE OIL SUPPLIES

The uncertainty of future North Sea oil supplies can hardly be overemphasised. The producing companies are working in a very difficult environment, to overcome which they are operating close to the frontiers of production technology. Consequently, one must expect delays to development and production programmes, unexpected technical problems on fields which are producing oil (such as corrosion, which seems to have afflicted equipment earlier than anticipated), and further accidents. Although the Ekofisk Bravo blow-out in the spring of 1977 is the only serious accident which has disrupted production, it would be over-optimistic to assume that output will build up smoothly into the 1980s with no further accidents. Britain is only at the beginning of exploiting its offshore area: the producing companies are having to learn from experience, as is the British Government, which is unaccustomed to dealing with a large indigenous oil supply.

A SURPRISE-FREE PROJECTION

Given the inherent technological uncertainties, the approach used in Chapter 3 of this book is to construct a 'surprise-free' supply projection which is then used as a benchmark against which the impact of changes in key variables can be judged. The projection (summarised in Figure 3.3) includes fields already under development, those considered likely to be developed and assumed future discoveries. Calculated output rates for individual fields should not be taken too seriously, since there is doubt about reserves-in-place, recovery factors and rates of depletion over time even for the fields already in production, but the aggregate supply estimates appear to be as reasonable an assessment as one can make from the limited exploration and production experience to date.

The essential messages of the surprise-free projection are as follows.

barring serious accidents, output from the fifteen established commercial fields should reach about 2 million barrels per day (100 million tonnes per year) by about 1980, which would be approximately equal to probable United Kingdom oil consumption in that year.

output from the fifteen fields can be expected to decline from the early 1980s but there are more than twenty potentially commercial fields already discovered, which should be in production by the early to mid-1980s and should bring British North Sea oil output to almost 3 million barrels per day (140 million tonnes per year) by about 1985. Assuming such fields are in production, North Sea oil output in the early 1980s is likely to exceed United Kingdom oil consumption, which will most probably be no more than 120 million tonnes a year.

a further output boost to over 3 million barrels per day (150 million tonnes per year) by the later 1980s might well result from exploration efforts, although future discoveries may be of smaller average size than already proved North Sea fields.

The surprise-free projection is confined to the North Sea area where significant oil discoveries have so far been made 50° 50′ North to 62° North and, as explained in Chapter 3, it makes a number of assumptions which are equivalent to the broad proposition that the environment in which the companies operate remains much as it is now.

GEOLOGICAL UNCERTAINTIES

There are many events which could disturb this surprise-free projection. Unfortunately, by the very nature of surprises one cannot define all of them, but a number are identified at various points in the book. One of the greatest uncertainties which will not be resolved for many years concerns future discoveries of oil. No one really knows what may eventually be found in the North Sea, still less what finds might occur in the offshore area to the west of the United Kingdom. The general view is that the westerly areas are not very promising[1] and that the North Sea proper will yield only relatively small discoveries but the opinions of even the best-informed observer contain large elements of speculation.

TAXATION

Abstracting from the geological imponderables, the sensitivity of North Sea oil supplies to key economic variables is investigated in Chapters 5, 6 and 7. In Chapter 5 the superficial similarities and the less obvious differences between the British and Norwegian oil taxation systems are discussed. A peculiarity of the British system is that both the government's percentage 'take' and company after-tax DCF returns appear to be very insensitive to variations in the rate of Petroleum Revenue Tax. Another significant difference from the Norwegian system is that, if oil prices were to fall sharply, the British royalty system would tend to increase percentage government 'take', even though PRT payments would be zero. It is not difficult to think of practical problems which may well arise in the operation of PRT and there are objections to the way the Government is attempting to extract rent from the North Sea producers (see the comments on pages 192–4 on licence allocation). Nevertheless, so far as one can tell, the companies working in the North Sea are not too unhappy with the tax structure established by the Oil Taxation Act of 1975. Provided there is no radical alteration in that structure, and assuming all other relevant variables are held constant, one would not expect minor variations in tax rates to have any substantial effect on the supplies of oil suggested in the surprise-free projection.

PRICES

There are a number of complications in analysing the effect on supplies of price variations with other variables held constant. First it is very difficult to make sensible assumptions about oil prices in the long-term future. Second, there is so little North Sea production experience that one cannot construct by econometric means a supply curve (with respect to price). Third, the effect of a given price change will vary according to its impact on price *expectations*. It is pointed out in Chapters 2 and 7 and later in this chapter that in a freely operating market price expectations play a crucial role in determining the rates at which producers plan to deplete their oil reservoirs. *Ceteris paribus*, a change in expectations towards lower prices in the future will increase current output from existing reserves but reduce future development and exploration effort, whereas higher expected prices will postpone the production of reserves but stimulate development and exploration. Chapter 6 attempts to deal with such complexities by resort to first principles and by the use of three price scenarios. All the scenarios contain expectations of rising oil prices in the 1980s and 1990s but one assumes a modest decline in the late 1970s: it is also assumed (unlike the surprise-free scenario) that there will be some measure of government depletion control so that owners of oil reservoirs have little or no freedom to vary their output rates with changes in their price expectations. In such circumstances it seems reasonable to assume that the principal effect of variations in actual and expected prices will be via their impact on profitability, with depletion profiles virtually unchanged.

A price fall in the late 1970s is unlikely greatly to affect supplies up to the mid-1980s, as compared with the surprise-free scenario. In a free market, producers might not wish to make any substantial shift from future to present production because their long term expectations are probably for increasing prices; in any case, such a shift might well not be allowed by the government. The high ratio of unavoidable to avoidable costs is likely to prevent owners of fields already in production from significantly reducing output at any price level one can contemplate in the next few years. A price fall, however, would be likely to reduce potential profitability and supplies from fields discovered but not yet under development (where most costs are avoidable) and exploration activity (where all costs are avoidable) would most likely be temporarily curtailed.

Similarly, if prices were to increase substantially relative to costs, anticipated profitability would tend to increase and (assuming no significant shift from present to future output for fields in production) the pace of development would probably quicken, making supplies by the mid-1980s rather greater than the surprise-free projection indicates. Exploration activity would no doubt also increase in such circumstances, so that, geology permitting, supplies in the late 1980s and 1990s might be greater than the highest curve in Figure 3.3.

DEPLETION CONTROL

The likely impact on supplies of the system of regulating output instituted by the Petroleum and Submarine Pipelines Act and other legislation (see Chapter 2) is also hard to assess because one cannot be sure how such open-ended laws will be put into practice. Chapter 7 uses the so-called 'Varley Guidelines' to calculate the effect on company after-tax returns and concludes that, provided control remains within the guidelines, production cuts are not likely to reduce company profitability severely. Development delays, combined with production cuts and associated cost increases might, however, have a considerably more serious effect.

The direct (intentional) impact of any regulation of production would be confined to reducing output rates by no more than 20 per cent, if the Varley guidelines are kept, but there would probably be unintended effects also. The surprise-free supply projection in Figure 3.3 assumes that companies are free to determine their own production rates. If they are not they will most likely be less willing to invest in fields already discovered and to carry out further exploration than under the surprise-free assumptions. Existence of a depletion control system (whether used or not) will tend to increase uncertainty for the producing companies, as explained in Chapter 7. A company considering a North Sea investment project *ex ante* would foresee the possibility of lower output rates and lower profitability than under a producer-determined depletion regime: its most probable estimate of the project's DCF return would therefore be lower and, *ceteris paribus*, the company would be less likely to invest.

The principal *intended* effect of depletion control within the Varley guidelines would be to spread the peak shown in Figure 3.3 over a slightly longer period. There would probably also be an *unintended* effect which would result in some loss of output because of the reduced incentive to invest in the North Sea, as compared with the surprise-free scenario. One can only guess at the scale of the loss which would depend on whether or not production cuts and development delays were implemented and whether or not producing companies believed the Varley guidelines would remain.

GENERAL CONCLUSIONS ON SUPPLIES

Output in the late 1970s and early 1980s is unlikely to be very elastic with respect to economic variables (although it might be affected by accidents) and it can reasonably be expected to build up to approximate equivalence to United Kingdom oil consumption. Farther ahead, the prospect is more uncertain. If one sets aside the possibility of major geological and technological surprises, the most likely reasons why supplies from the mid-1980s onwards might differ from the surprise-free scenario seem to be variations in oil prices relative to costs and depletion control. The error margins around the surprise-free scenario are bound to be wide, but are difficult to estimate. One might subjectively assess them at ± 20 per cent in the mid to late 1980s; that is, approximately ± 30 million tonnes per annum around the top curve in Figure 3.3.

GOVERNMENT POLICY TOWARDS NORTH SEA OIL

POLICY IN GENERAL

Government policy towards energy in general, and towards the North Sea in particular, is a controversial matter. In earlier chapters various aspects of oil policy are discussed in detail; it is now time to give a more general view in the light of the earlier findings. At the same time some comments are made on official attitudes towards North Sea natural gas, since there are certain strands in the evolution of North Sea policy which are common both to oil and gas.

For twenty-five or more years after the Second World War the energy policies of successive British governments were dominated by a belief that the coal industry should be protected from the competition of other fuels.[2] In the early post-war years the objective was to expand coal output; subsequently, the more limited aim of avoiding a rapid decline in the industry took over.

Such policies were evidently not very successful since, despite a costly protective barrier which was constructed around coal, there was a very sharp fall in consumption, output and employment from the mid-1950s onwards – mainly because of competition from lower-priced oil. Table 9.1 illustrates some of the main trends in United Kingdom primary energy consumption since 1946: in those thirty years coal's share of the energy market fell from over 90 per cent to less than 40 per cent. Nevertheless, it was argued by Ministers that supporting coal would improve the balance of payments (as compared with importing oil), give greater security of supply, insure against oil price increases in the long term and help to ease the social and human problems of decline in a major industry. It is not appropriate here to express opinions on how valid were these reasons. What is more relevant is to point out two features of energy policy which reappeared in attitudes towards North Sea oil – a strong element of nationalism and a tendency in both large

TABLE 9.1 United Kingdom Inland Primary Energy Consumption

	1946		1956		1966		1971		1976	
	million tons coal equivalent	% of total	million tons coal equivalent	% of total	million tons coal equivalent	% of total	million tons coal equivalent	% of total	million tons coal equivalent	% of total
Coal	186	93	214	85	174	58	137	42	120	37
Oil	14	7	38	15	113	38	149	46	132	40
Hydro	1	—	1	—	2	1	2	1	2	1
Nuclear	—	—	—	—	8	3	9	3	13	4
Natural Gas	—	—	—	—	1	—	28	8	58	18
	201	100	253	100	298	100	325	100	325	100

SOURCES Robinson, *A Policy for Fuel?* (London: Institute of Economic Affairs, 1969) Table 1; and *Digest of UK Energy Statistics* (London: Department of Energy, various issues).

political parties to believe that there is something special about the energy industries which must mark them out for particular attention by the Government.

In the early days of North Sea exploitation, when the southern gas fields were being developed during the 1960s (see Chapter 2), policy continued to be dominated by a belief in coal protection. However, a gradually increasing element of nationalism crept into the issue of North Sea licences, and government regulation of the area was increased, as one might have predicted on the basis of previous policy towards the energy industries. By the mid-1970s the advent of the so-called energy 'crisis' and a realisation that Britain had access to large quantities of offshore oil had placed the North Sea in the forefront of policy. Moreover, the coal industry received a degree of protection from the actions of OPEC which was far greater than British governments had ever contrived. The 'crisis' encouraged the belief that there are massive problems in the energy market which require detailed government intervention[3] and the discovery of substantial British oil and gas reserves led those of a *dirigiste* frame of mind to conclude that there had opened up a new freedom to 'plan' the country's energy future[4] and, indeed, its economic future. There are three particularly important areas of North Sea policy which are discussed briefly below.

ALLOCATING NORTH SEA LICENCES

The issue of licences to explore for and produce hydrocarbons is usually the first significant step in the exploitation of a new petroleum province. Except in the United States,[5] petroleum resources are generally owned by the state and the Government awards licences to private operators to develop any commercially-exploitable petroleum reserves there may be. One would expect the method chosen to allocate such licences to be crucial to the evolution of official policy towards the area. So it proved to be in the United Kingdom. To understand how British policy towards the North Sea has developed it is necessary to look back to the early days of licensing in the southern part of the area.

As Kenneth Dam has explained,[6] in a powerful critique of the British allocation system, it seems to have been assumed in official circles from the first round of North Sea licensing in 1964 that the natural order dictates allocation of rights to produce oil by administrators' 'discretion' rather than by a market system, and the favouring of British interests relative to those of foreigners.

The history of North Sea licensing can be explained here very briefly because of the excellent account written by Professor Dam. In 1964, Frederick Erroll, as Conservative Minister of Power, laid down some rather loose criteria for allocating North Sea blocks which, as Dam says, were ' . . . merely statements of the preferences and predilections that were to guide the ministry in making its awards [embodying] . . . a major political consideration: the extent to which foreign-controlled oil interests were to be permitted to reap profits from Britain's natural resources.'[7] There were strong nationalistic undertones. Erroll wanted 'substantial British participation' and said he aimed to protect the 'national interest'. The allocation criteria stated, *inter alia*, that the applicant should be making some contribution towards development of the Continental Shelf and the British energy market generally. Clearly, there was enormous scope under such a system of awards for civil servants to make subjective judgements about the worthiness of applicants.

As further rounds of licensing proceeded, the system of award by administrative discretion was retained, apart from a very limited experiment with auctioning fifteen blocks (out of a total of 282) in the 1971 Fourth Round, but the nationalistic element increased. For instance, in the 1965 Second Round preference was given to applicants in groups in which nationalised industries participated, and in the 1969 Third Round the Government insisted that the (then) Gas Council or the National Coal Board should participate in any Irish Sea licences and gave further preference to North Sea groups with Gas Council, National Coal Board or other British interests. By the time of the 1977 Fifth Round, 51 per cent participation by the recently-formed British National Oil Corporation or the British Gas Corporation (previously the Gas Council and Area Boards) had become a condition of any licence award; moreover, companies which wanted Fifth Round blocks were expected to reach participation agreements for finds made under licences issued in previous rounds.

There was a clear trend for the preference given to British interests, and particularly to the nationalised industries, to increase with each successive licence issue. Throughout the licence rounds, the system gave considerable power to civil servants to hand out valuable licences on rather vague criteria. Although there was some competition among applicants in terms of work programmes,[8] and small rental payments had to be made for production licences, a rationing scheme by administrators was the rule in the issue of North Sea licences.

It is worth considering why virtually all North Sea licence awards have been made at administrative discretion, rather than by the alternative of competitive bidding. Licences to explore for and (if there are discoveries) produce oil or gas are valuable rights to property for which the oil companies would have been prepared to bid substantial sums had the licences been auctioned, as the restricted auction of 1971 demonstrated.[9] The auction system has many attractions to the economist. As Dam points out, competitive bidding in the absence of collusion should lead to the state's receiving a large part of any economic rent accruing from oil and gas production. It is true that in the early days of exploration and development of any new petroleum province, lack of knowledge will make it difficult for potential bidders to know what value to place on the available land. However, companies can bid what they believe to be the values of areas on offer (after allowing for risk). In any case, no one should expect perfect solutions in an imperfect world and the auction seems a good, if rough-and-ready, method of extracting rent as knowledge accumulates. Competitive bidding for licences will allocate licences, collect the rent and favour low-cost potential licensees who can outbid the competition.

Although there are various popular objections to auctioning licences and bidding is apparently disliked by the British Government and the oil companies, the overt objections seem rather weak. For example, there appears to be little evidence for the view that auctions collect money which would otherwise have been used for exploration. Only if governments were to collect significantly less rent through taxation than they would have received from competitive bidding might drilling be stimulated but, as Dam observes, it would then presumably rise above the optimum.[10]

The reasons why competitive bidding has not been used in Britain probably have little to do with the economic analysis of the effects of auctions versus discretionary allocation. On economic efficiency grounds there may be a strong case for selling valuable properties in the North Sea, thereby relieving the authorities of the need to employ officials to judge the worthiness of applicants and to devise complicated tax systems (such as Petroleum Revenue Tax — see Chapters 4 and 5) to extract rent.[11] Those versed in the economic theory of democracy[12] will have little difficulty in explaining the unpopularity of licence auctions. As Dam says, the discretionary regime in Britain has been used for nationalistic purposes and for informal arm-twisting of the oil companies. It is not hard to see other reasons why politicians and civil servants dislike auctions.[13] One thing above all which characterises the discretionary system and distinguishes it from competitive bidding is the considerable power and influence it gives to those who administer it: no matter how well-meaning are the administrators, to them auctioning must seem too simple, too likely to remove control from their hands and too likely to reduce their numbers and promotion opportunities. Licence allocation is a prime example of the point made in Chapter 2 that, given the powerful position which civil servants and politicians have in society today, their pursuit of self-interest may have unfortunate effects on the rest of the community.

PRICING NORTH SEA GAS

Although this book is primarily concerned with *oil* from the North Sea, the licence allocation system just described had some effects on North

Sea *natural gas* in the 1960s and 1970s which need brief explanation, since they demonstrate how initial attempts to suppress the operation of a market frequently create new problems which government then tries to solve by further intervention. [14]

Given that the British government decided not to use a market system to allocate North Sea licences, it faced itself with the problem, once substantial gas discoveries had been made in the southern North Sea, that the licences had been virtually given away so that any rent there might be would accrue to the companies. There is room for argument about how to determine whether rent exists and about the advantages and disadvantages of channelling it to the State, but the British Government was clearly alarmed at the prospect of overseas oil companies making 'excess' profits from the North Sea.

Consequently, the (then) Minister of Power appears to have decided that the nationalised gas industry should be used to collect the rent by a very strict interpretation of the 1964 Continental Shelf Act: the companies were effectively denied the opportunity to sell their product to anyone other than the Gas Council, with the minor exception of non-fuel uses. [15] Thus, a state monopsonist became the instrument of rent collection, and the Ministry involved itself in the detailed negotiations during the years 1966–8 so as to ensure that the Council took a hard line with the oil companies.

Despite stout resistance by the oil companies, in the end they inevitably succumbed to the attentions of the sole buyer. The price established for natural gas in 1968 of around 1.2p/therm (at the United Kingdom coast), was very low in relation to energy prices then ruling: for example, it was only about two thirds of the c.i.f. price of imported crude oil, which is an inferior product to natural gas and requires refining as well as distribution and marketing. There was some increase in the British Gas Corporation's purchase price in the 1970s but because of soaring oil prices (see Chapter 1) by the mid-1970s it had declined to 15 to 20 per cent of the imported crude price. [16]

In Britain the popular view seems to be that it is desirable to pay the minimum price possible to foreign oil companies for natural gas: no doubt it is believed that the British consumer benefits thereby. The issue, however, is much more complex. If, for the sake of argument it is accepted that rent is available and should be removed from the companies it should presumably accrue to the state, on which one then relies to use it wisely. There can hardly be a case for transferring rent from certain large corporations which happen to be privately owned to another large corporation which happens to be nationalised. But if the rent flows initially to the nationalised corporation how is one to know that some or all does not remain there? It would be naive to assume that the Gas Corporation would simply sell at market prices, make large profits and have them taxed away by the government: indeed the evidence shows that the Corporation was not particularly profitable although, outside times of government price restraint, it appears to have sold natural gas at close to market prices. It is no criticism of the Gas Corporation, which merely operated within ground-rules laid down by governments, to say that the price it paid for natural gas was so low that it lacked any proper standard of efficiency.

There have been so many complicating factors in recent years – such as government price control – that it is impossible to draw quantitative conclusions about where the rent came to rest. Nevertheless, anyone with knowledge of large organisations would feel confident that the distribution and marketing costs of the Gas Corporation are most probably higher than they would have been at a natural gas purchase price more in line with other energy prices. In other words, what would otherwise have been rent in private corporations appears to have been translated in whole or in part into organisational slack in a nationalised corporation.[17]

One other effect of the low-price policy for natural gas is perhaps more obvious. Exploration effort in the southern North Sea declined sharply after 1969:[18] to some extent this may have been because companies did not believe there would be any more large gas finds, but there is little doubt that they preferred to look in northern waters for oil which they were not obliged to sell to the nationalised gas industry.[19] It is not clear whether this indicates that the natural gas price was so low that the returns obtained by the companies were below their opportunity costs of capital. Nevertheless, it does at least indicate that in comparison with one opportunity – to invest in North Sea oil exploration and, where this was successful, production – returns from natural gas investment were thought to be low.

DEPLETION CONTROL

British governments' attitudes towards depletion can now be seen as part of North Sea policy as a whole (which is not necessarily to say that the overall policy is internally consistent). What began as an attempt to control licence awards by judging the worthiness of applicants produced the prospect of excess profits. Governments then felt it necessary – to solve this problem which they had created – to use a nationalised industry (for gas) and the taxation system (for oil) in an effort to capture what they believe to be rent. The licensing system itself became steadily more favourable to British and especially nationalised industry interests: this may be rationalised in economic terms as an attempt to keep profits in Britain, but it seems also to have been intended to secure greater British control of the North Sea.

The next stage was to institute a depletion control mechanism (discussed in Chapter 2). By the mid-1970s there appears to have been a consensus in Britain in favour of some such control but, as Chapters 2 and 7 explain, there are many difficulties in the way of successful output regulation and it may lead to considerable uncertainty. It is possible to take an optimistic view of such regulation: it might be argued that company profitability may not be significantly reduced, that the producers may learn to live with the political uncertainties as they have in other parts of the world, and that the extra resource costs may turn out to be small. This *is* an optimistic rather than the most probable view of the costs of regulating production. Furthermore, it is not clear what benefits, if any, regulation will bring. There is no reason to believe that the Department of Energy's efforts to improve on the production plans of the oil companies will actually provide net gains for the British people. Although the Minister will take the name of the 'national interest' if he decides to regulate North Sea production, it is unlikely that he can attribute any objective meaning to such an elusive concept. It is quite conceivable, *pace* the popular wisdom, that the Department's efforts will result in a *less* desirable depletion rate than would have been achieved by the companies, left to themselves.

To say this is not in any way to argue that the market will achieve an 'optimum' rate of depletion (whatever that may mean) or even that it will work smoothly. One must accept that markets work very imperfectly but, as Chapter 2 explains, everything in this world (including governments) is imperfect, so it is an irrelevance to single out the market for criticism on such grounds. Logically, one should compare the likely effects of an imperfect market with those of an imperfect government.

One of the advantages of market-determined depletion rates is that price signals should, on the whole, move consumers and producers *in the right direction* (see Chapter 2). It is, of course, possible to specify models in which a resource market works perversely.[20] For example, say that a rise in the price of some resource is thought by producers to be temporary. They are then likely, especially if they are risk-averse, to *increase* their output to take advantage of what they perceive to be a temporarily good market situation. Price rises will then tend to increase the rate of depletion and price falls might reduce it. However, producers' behaviour will, *ceteris paribus*, depend on their price expectations, and perverse behaviour could hardly continue for long if real resource scarcity were developing, unless the producers were incapable of learning.

As the resource was seen to be becoming scarce, expectations of price rises would be formed and existing producers would tend to restrict output, hopefully conserving the resource until such time as substitutes appeared and price expectations changed. At the same time, exploration activity and the development of new resources would be stimulated by enhanced profitability. There does not seem to be any evidence that the oil and gas markets work perversely. On the contrary, the energy 'crisis' seems to be demonstrating the power of market forces to conserve energy in the face of rising prices.[21] Indeed, it is significant that some of the principal difficulties in the adjustment process have stemmed not from imperfections in the market but from legacies of past government intervention, such as the control of fuel prices which has operated both in Britain and the United States.

Moreover, there are ways in which fuel markets could be made to operate more efficiently — principally by increasing the degree of competition to which producers are subject.[22] At the same time, fuel markets would more closely reflect real costs if a greater government effort were made to internalise the social costs of pollution in the energy industries. Some of the difficulties of doing this were mentioned in Chapter 2 but there is little doubt that governments could, on the basis of existing scientific knowledge, impose much stricter pollution controls. While there is no guarantee that such action would be efficient, nor that it would move the depletion rate for North Sea oil and gas closer to the optimum (because one cannot be sure of the directions of the effects of other imperfections), one might judge that the dangers of irreversible pollution are large enough for this to be a desirable course of action.

It is not so easy to see how the efficiency of government action can be improved. As explained in Chapter 2, there are strong self-generating forces in government activity and serious dangers lie in the pursuit of personal interests by those in the public sector no matter how well-intentioned they are: one of the great unsolved problems of the day is that of *quis custodiet ipsos custodes*. It is popularly believed that oil companies will deplete North Sea resources 'too rapidly' (see Chapter 2) so that an enlightened Government should act to reduce output below company plans. The rationale of this view is rarely made explicit but presumably its exponents assume an increasing scarcity of fuel and substantial future price increases: however, since these are precisely the circumstances in which, in a freely-functioning market, known resources would tend to be conserved for future generations and new resources would be sought, it is not clear what additional action is needed (other than to help the market to work better). Even if one believes that the central authorities are better at forecasting than the market is (in itself a doubtful proposition), there is no guarantee that they will be able to determine a 'national interest' depletion policy nor that they would necessarily put such a policy into effect. Indeed, some surprising results might arise from central regulation of depletion.

As an illustration, consider how a rational politician might view depletion control. One possibility is that he believes he can win popularity by well-publicised moves to restrict output: he might calculate that taking a hard line with foreign oil companies exploiting 'our' resources would appeal to nationalistic instincts in the populace. Another type of political calculus which would lead to opposite results might be to consider what macroeconomic benefits depletion control could transfer from the present to the future. Politicians know that they and their parties will not hold office for ever. Consequently, if they reduce output they run the risk of transferring some of the economic gains from North Sea oil to a time when another party can claim them for its own.[23] The following example illustrates the point.

In Chapter 8, the balance-of-payments effects of North Sea oil were computed on various assumptions about oil output, prices and other variables. In the following example, the Crude Price Indexation price scenario and the all-fields production case are taken (as in Table 8.3) and the balance-of-payments gains are recalculated on the assumption that depletion control is in operation. Specifically, it is assumed that the established commercial fields are subject to 20 per cent output reductions from 1982 onwards; that output from the potentially commercial fields is also reduced by 20 per cent from 1982 or four years after the start of production (whichever is later); that development delays of the sort assumed in Chapter 7 are imposed on new discoveries; and that there is no production from 100 million barrel fields (see Chapter 3).

Table 9.2 shows the difference which depletion control would, on the specified assumptions, make to the current and long-term capital account balance. From 1982 onwards, when output reductions are assumed to begin, there is a significant and increasing decline in the estimated balance of payments gain from North Sea oil. Although one can argue about the assumptions which should be made about the extent of depletion control, so that the numbers shown should only be regarded as indicating orders of magintude, it is obvious that imposing output cuts will involve giving up potential economic gains 'now' and moving them into the future. It is one thing to talk now about cutting production in the 1980s: depending on Britain's economic situation then it may seem a distinctly less attractive prospect when the 1980s arrive.

One of the greatest dangers of central regulation of output is that decisions could be made on the basis of all manner of calculations which may be very rational in political terms but have little to do with the 'national interest' which is supposed to be the object of the exercise. There is no useful prediction one can offer of how control will be operated, which is another way of saying that it adds another dimension of uncertainty to those involved in North Sea activities.

GENERAL CONCLUSIONS ON GOVERNMENT POLICY

British government policy towards North Sea oil has evolved from the early days of natural gas discoveries towards much greater central regulation. The range of weapons now available to a determined Government is formidable and ministerial power is subject to minimal

TABLE 9.2 Estimated Impact of North Sea Oil on the United Kingdom
Balance of Payments (NS minus nNS)[a]
Crude Price Indexation Scenario with Production from All Fields

| | Current and Long-term Capital Balance | | |
| | *(£'000 million at current prices)* | | |
	With no depletion control[b]	With depletion control[c]	Difference
	(1)	(2)	(2) minus (1)
1980	5.6	5.6	−
1981	7.0	7.0	−
1982	8.6	7.4	− 1.2
1983	8.9	6.8	− 2.1
1984	9.3	7.0	− 2.3
1985	10.0	7.3	− 2.7
1986	11.3	8.0	− 3.3
1987	12.2	8.6	− 3.6
1988	13.4	8.7	− 4.7
1989	13.6	8.5	− 5.1
1990	13.2	8.7	− 4.5

[a] The nature of the estimates is explained in Chapter 8.
[b] From Table 8.3.
[c] See p. 199 for an explanation of the type of control.

SOURCE Authors' estimates.

checks. It is not obvious that the regulatory system has arisen from public demand or from economic logic. More realistically, it can be seen as a consequence of the self-interest of politicians and administrators – not because they are in any way malevolent but because of the relatively few checks and balances to which they are today subject.

Of course, the appearance of a regime for the wrong reasons is only a necessary (not a sufficient) condition for regarding it as undesirable. In the ultimate, whether one veers towards 'market' or 'planning' solutions is largely a matter of one's own value judgements, aided by such evidence and experience as one can muster. The authors' judgement is that better results are likely to flow from a system of diffused power which channels personal self-interests in desirable directions rather than from a system of central direction which concentrates power in the hands of a few people who can plead pursuit of the 'national interest' for any of their actions. [24] A leaning towards market solutions by no means excludes significant government intervention – indeed, official action to encourage competition and to internalise social costs would be stimulated – but one would expect such intervention and its effects to be carefully considered. No doubt vast amounts of time have been devoted within government to thoughts about North Sea policy, but there is no evidence of any objective assessment of the relative places of government and market forces.

Few people would urge unrestrained competition and complete government withdrawal from oversight of North Sea development. It is more reasonable to seek for ways in which market forces could be allowed more play and to attempt to improve the functioning of the market so as to move away from the pretence – from which massive errors can so easily flow – that a small group of people can readily see what is good for the British nation. Some suggestions are made earlier in this chapter. For instance there appear to be strong arguments for changing the North Sea licence award system to competitive bidding. Certain consequential changes would then flow from this fundamental move because the discretionary allocation regime already has features designed to extract rent. The Petroleum Revenue Tax, which as Chapters 4 and 5 showed, is a complicated device, could be abandoned and the British Gas Corporation's position as sole buyer of natural gas would need to be altered. A relatively straightforward change would be to allow natural gas producers to sell their product direct to industrial users (not to the household market, which would probably be impractical), thereby significantly increasing competition for British Gas and other companies in the energy market. Potential oil and gas producers would thus bid for licences and those which made discoveries would have reasonable freedom to dispose of their products, subject to the same taxes as other United Kingdom companies. There would be no need for restrictions on crude oil exports.

Depletion control introduces additional uncertainty into North Sea activities and places enormous power in ministerial hands. Although most economists would accept that circumstances *might* arise in which there should be some control on production, they should be the exception rather than the rule; consequently there seems no reason to keep the detailed regulatory apparatus of the Petroleum and Submarine Pipelines Act. The prime need seems to be to institute a reserve power to control depletion which contains safeguards against arbitrary government decisions. In the absence of some judicial means of checking ministerial power there could, for example, be a procedure whereby a minister who wishes to alter the production programmes of the companies is obliged to hold a public hearing and then give detailed reasons for any decision he reaches. On such important issues, decisions behind closed doors should not be possible. Public debate and public explanation should be required: no one who claims to be working in the 'national interest' should want it otherwise.

NORTH SEA OIL AND THE BRITISH ECONOMY

Although this book is aimed principally at analysing the microeconomics of North Sea oil and government policy towards exploitation of the area, it concludes with some very brief comments on the macroeconomic implications.

Since it became clear that the United Kingdom would be a middle-rank oil producer by the early 1980s, opinions about the impact of oil on the economy have varied widely from time to time and some significant differences of view have emerged between those who regard the North Sea as the saviour of Britain's economy and those who believe it might have little effect or even be harmful.

To a limited extent it is possible to quantify the future influence of oil on the economy. In Chapter 8 the potential balance-of-payments effects are estimated on a variety of assumptions. The calculations are designed to emphasise a point which is left unclear in official estimates — that the effect is extremely sensitive to the assumptions one makes about oil prices and oil output. They demonstrate that, on the assumptions specified in Chapter 8, the potential current and long-term capital account gain from North Sea oil in the mid-1980s might lie in the range £6–15,000 million or approximately 2 to 6 per cent of GNP at that time. It can also be estimated that the potential effect of North Sea oil on the United Kingdom's rate of real GNP growth might be of the order of $\frac{1}{2}$ to 1 per cent per annum from the mid-1970s to the mid-1980s (as compared with a situation of no North Sea oil).[25]

One should, however, show a proper humility in making any such estimates. The uncertainties associated with the North Sea itself, which are repeatedly stressed in earlier chapters, are daunting enough: the technology is in its early days, the geology is only partially known, one can only make informed guesses at future costs, prices and government policy. But, in considering the macroeconomic impact of North Sea oil an extra layer of uncertainty is added. It was argued in an earlier publication by the authors that ' . . . the greatest uncertainties about the impact of North Sea oil on the British economy relate not so much to the volume of oil that will be produced, and at what price it will be sold, but to how efficiently the British economy will be managed as its new-found "riches" begin to flow in large volume.'[26]

GOVERNMENT OIL REVENUES

One thing that seems reasonably certain is that the tax system described in Chapters 4 and 5 will bring in substantial sums to the British Government. About 60 to 70 per cent of company net revenues is likely to accrue to the government (Table 5.1). As North Sea activities are likely to be significantly more profitable than the activities in which United Kingdom resources would have been employed in the absence of North Sea oil, most of the tax receipts can be taken as additional government income.

Table 9.3 gives estimates of British government revenue from royalties, Petroleum Revenue Tax and Corporation Tax on the North Sea producers.[27] The calculations are consistent with those made in earlier chapters. Corporation Tax is calculated on a field rather than a company basis which, as explained in Chapter 5, will tend to over-estimate actual tax payments in the early years.

As in the case of the balance-of-payments estimates a wide range of variation in government tax receipts from North Sea oil is possible, depending on the oil output and oil price assumptions used. Tax revenues are given in Table 9.3 for the two price/output combinations used in Chapter 8 (pages 180–1) to establish a plausible range for the balance-of-payments estimates. The low end of the range, which assumes some decline in oil prices up to 1980 and no further discoveries, yields annual tax revenues in the early 1980s of £2–4000 million, split roughly equally between royalty, PRT[28] and Corporation Tax. By the mid-1980s, however, Corporation Tax payments substantially exceed those from each of the other two sources. At the top end of the range, with much higher oil prices and new North Sea discoveries, government revenues are two to three times as high in the 1980s as in the low case. By the late 1980s Corporation Tax receipts exceed those from PRT but earlier receipts from the two taxes are of similar size. To provide some basis for comparison, government receipts from VAT in 1976–77 were £3770 million, from Corporation Tax £2660 million and from the alcoholic drink and hydrocarbon oil duties about £2000 million each: thus, even at the low end of the range shown in Table 9.3, receipts from North Sea oil are substantial compared with the present large revenue-raisers. Although receipts from present taxes will increase, it seems clear that by the late 1970s a very large new source of government revenues will have appeared.[29]

POTENTIAL AND ACTUAL BENEFITS

There is a strong temptation for anyone who calculates these large figures of balance-of-payments gains and increasing tax revenues to believe that North Sea oil is a crock of gold presented to the British people by a beneficent Almighty: the only question, on this view, is how to distribute this unexpected blessing. The impact effect of North Sea oil has encouraged this belief. For example, during 1977 a substantial improvement in the United Kingdom's balance of payments occurred, largely because of the initial effects of North Sea oil output in reducing oil imports. In January-December 1977 net imports of crude oil were 54

TABLE 9.3 Government Revenues from North Sea Oil (£'000 million)

	Limited Price Decline Scenario Production from Established and Potentially Commercial Fields[a]				Use of Monopoly Power Scenario Production from all Fields[b]			
	Royalty	PRT	Corporation Tax	Total	Royalty	PRT	Corporation Tax	Total
1975	–	–	–	–	–	–	–	–
1976	0.1	–	–	0.1	0.1	–	–	0.1
1977	0.3	–	–	0.3	0.3	–	–	0.3
1978	0.5	0.5	0.5	1.5	0.7	0.6	0.5	1.8
1979	0.6	0.7	0.8	2.1	0.9	1.1	1.1	3.1
1980	0.7	0.8	0.9	2.4	1.2	1.6	1.5	4.3
1981	0.8	0.9	0.9	2.6	1.4	2.3	2.5	6.2
1982	0.9	1.0	1.4	3.3	1.6	3.1	3.0	7.7
1983	1.0	1.5	1.7	4.2	1.9	3.1	3.0	8.0
1984	1.1	1.1	1.3	3.5	2.2	3.4	3.7	9.3
1985	1.1	0.9	1.7	3.7	2.5	3.7	4.2	10.4
1990	0.8	0.8	2.3	3.9	3.0	5.6	7.9	16.5

[a] Corresponding to Table 8.5.
[b] Corresponding to Table 8.9.

SOURCE Authors' estimates.

million tonnes, compared with 86 million tonnes in the corresponding months of 1976. As these initial benefits were realised there was a notable increase in optimism about the prospects for the British economy, encouraged by ministerial speeches, and various interest groups in the community began staking their claims to the distribution of riches they evidently believed was to come.

It is, of course, true that North Sea oil gives the United Kingdom the potential to raise its real GNP above what it would have been without the North Sea. In effect, North Sea discoveries present relatively good investment opportunities so that the employment of resources in oil production and associated activities is almost certainly more productive than the alternative uses for such resources in the absence of North Sea oil. In addition, some resources which would otherwise have been idle may be employed. Thus the economy should move closer to the production possibility frontier. In Chapter 8 the potential gain to the economy is measured in terms of the balance of payments but there is no necessary reason why benefits should be realised in this way. After the impact effect on overseas payments, the influence of North Sea oil will spread through the economy in ways which are difficult to envisage because they depend on the behaviour of government, industry and millions of people. There is no reason to believe that the eventual effect will be of the same order of magnitude as the impact effect: it is even possible for a favourable impact to be translated into an adverse final effect.

In practice, it is very unlikely that the gains from North Sea oil will all flow into the balance of payments, as the calculations in Chapter 8 might seem to imply. Although the United Kingdom's balance-of-payments position in the mid-1970s clearly leaves much room for improvement, there would be no point in accumulating large payments surpluses — which, apart from their 'beggar-thy-neighbour' aspect, would earn only low rates of interest. One extreme possibility is that the bulk of the initial gain from North Sea oil flows into profitable non-North Sea investment projects, the United Kingdom's international competitiveness improves and the rate of economic growth increases. In this happy state the accruing gains from North Sea oil would be invested and multiplied.

On a more pessimistic view, one could envisage a rising money supply generated by the impact effect of North Sea oil which is increased still further by a Government anxious to reduce unemployment and to remain in office. For a time, there might be real gains in consumption but, assuming that the rate of inflation would be increased (as compared with a no-North Sea oil state), most of the benefits might well disappear. In other words, because of a change in government behaviour as a consequence of North Sea oil, much of the potential gain could be dissipated. Another pessimistic view is that the sterling exchange rate will appreciate as more North Sea oil flows and that the elasticities of demand for United Kingdom imports and exports are such that appreciation will worsen the non-oil balance of payments. It is even conceivable that the overall balance of payments will, in a few years' time, be worse with North Sea oil than it would otherwise have been.

Neither the extremely optimistic nor the extremely pessimistic outcome seems particularly likely: such cases are of interest primarily to demonstrate how wide is the area of uncertainty. What is important is to ensure that some significant gain to the economy is realised from North Sea oil. In the earlier parts of this chapter it is suggested that a misplaced desire by successive governments for detailed intervention – evidently in pursuit of 'control' over foreign companies – has detracted from the efficiency of North Sea exploitation. Similar problems may well arise over government macroeconomic policy in an era of North Sea oil. There appears to be strong support for the view that the Government should adopt a more interventionist stance towards industry, using North Sea benefits for selective assistance and providing yet more subsidies to investment.[30] The most extreme example of the 'crock of gold' mentality is the proposal that a North Sea development fund should be established from which those who are judged worthy can be given handouts.[31] It is extraordinary that such ideas can flourish when all the evidence of recent years suggests that government-sponsored investment is unlikely to be profitable.

Although in a book primarily devoted to the microeconomic aspects of North Sea oil the macroeconomic implications have necessarily been discussed only very briefly, it is the authors' view that the last thing Britain needs is a detailed government strategy for British industry based on a share-out of supposed North Sea benefits. There is no more reason to believe that the assembled multitudes of Ministers and civil servants (even when joined by the Confederation of British Industry, the Trades Union Congress and miscellaneous academics) can work out the 'correct' strategy for Britain and pick industrial winners than there is to think that the Energy Department can determine the 'optimum' depletion rate for North Sea oil.

In our judgement, a strategy more likely to succeed – although it lacks the optical advantage which central planning has of apparently being terribly busy in solving everyone's problems – would be much less interventionist. Macroeconomic policy would concentrate on allowing room for increased investment in fixed assets and in balance-of-payments improvement by restraining the growth of private and public consumption. The exchange rate would, by and large, be allowed to find its own level. Direct taxation would be reduced somewhat to sharpen incentives; however, since if fixed investment is to increase and the balance of payments is to improve there will have to be a rise in savings in the economy, big cuts may not be possible for some time, despite the large flow of North Sea revenues. If in such circumstances there were little increase in investment in Britain, the answer might well be, as Samuel Brittan, the British economic journalist, has suggested,[32] to remove controls on British investment abroad. One of the prime objectives of macroeconomic policy in an era of North Sea oil is that a substantial part of the initial gains should be invested profitably: if investment opportunities really are lacking in Britain it would be better to invest well abroad, thus providing an income for post-North Sea days, rather than to have well-meaning bureaucrats trying to tempt industrialists to invest by means of higher and higher subsidies. With the whole world to choose from, a good return on investment should be possible.

It must be admitted that any argument about how far government control of the economy should extend inevitably involves a great deal of subjective judgement. It cannot be resolved solely by what are traditionally regarded as 'economic' principles. Nevertheless, it is our view that the kinds of extensions of central control which are now being discussed and excused by reference to the need to 'take advantage of North Sea oil' go far beyond the bounds of what can be justified on economic efficiency grounds. Most likely, they are part of the same self-perpetuating process of state intervention in the private sector which is discussed in this chapter and which appears increasingly to surround all aspects of North Sea exploitation.

It would be a catastrophe if the potential benefits which could flow to Britain from the discovery of North Sea oil and which have arrived almost at an ideal moment were largely to disappear because of the tightening grip of political-cum-bureaucratic embrace. It is so easy to claim that market 'imperfections' make government intervention essential: it requires more sophistication to recognise the mainsprings of much of the intervention which actually occurs and to see that more freely operating markets have many advantages. In the words of that great economist Harry G. Johnson, ' . . . the defects of market organisation seem obvious to anyone, or can be made to seem so, whereas the socio-economic functions of the market are obscure and difficult to appreciate . . . to the bureaucratic mind the functioning of the price system as a regulator appears mere disorder and chaos'.[33] One of the most disturbing features of the belief in greater state control as a means of reaping the benefits of North Sea oil is the naïve acceptance, encouraged by government, that there is a body of central planners who can be relied upon to recognise and pursue the 'national interest'. Ambition, in its place, can be a fine virtue in our rulers. Quite a different matter, however, is excessive confidence in the effectiveness of central forecasting and planning. In conjunction with the powerful self-generating forces which already favour central intervention such ideas could well have the most unfortunate of consequences.

NOTES AND REFERENCES

1. It was announced in September 1977 that Shell and other companies have handed back Celtic Sea licences because of the number of 'dry holes' drilled in the area. See *Financial Times*, London, 10 September 1977.
2. See Robinson, *A Policy for Fuel?* (London: Institute of Economic Affairs, 1969) and *Competition for Fuel* (London: Institute of Economic Affairs, 1971).
3. Discussed in Robinson, *The Energy 'Crisis' and British Coal*, (London: Institute of Economic Affairs, 1974).
4. For example, Frances Morrell and Francis Cripps, 'The Case for a Planned Energy Policy', *National Energy Conference*, London, June 1976.
5. New petroleum resources in the United States are now frequently discovered either on federal land or on land owned by states, such as Alaska.
6. Kenneth W. Dam, *Oil Resources: Who Gets What How?* (Chicago and London: University of Chicago Press, 1976).
7. *Ibid.*, p. 25. Frederick Erroll's five criteria were:

   First, the need to encourage the most rapid and thorough exploration and economical exploitation of petroleum resources on the continental shelf. Second, the requirement that the applicant for a licence shall be incorporated in the United Kingdom and the profits of the operations shall be taxed here. Thirdly, in cases where the applicant is a foreign-owned concern, how far British oil companies receive equitable treatment in that country. Fourthly, we shall look at the programme of work of the applicant and also at the ability and resources to implement it. Fifthly, we shall look at the contribution the applicant has already made and is making towards the development of resources of our continental shelf and the development of our fuel economy generally.

8. *Ibid.*, pp. 28 and 32–6.
9. *Ibid.*, pp. 32–43.
10. *Ibid.*, p. 35.
11. Under a bidding regime the North Sea producers would presumably be taxed only at the same rate as the rest of British industry. They would not have the rent removed twice, as it were. One of the reasons why oil companies express a dislike for competitive bidding may well be that they fear that a switch to licence auctions would not be accompanied by reduced taxation.
12. For example, Anthony Downs, *An Economic Theory of Democracy*, (New York: Harper & Row, 1957).
13. See Robinson, review of Dam, *op. cit.*, *Journal of Political Economy*, Chicago, August 1977.
14. For further discussion of North Sea gas pricing see Dam, *op. cit.*, especially Chapter 8; Robinson, *Competition for Fuel*, *op. cit.*, pp. 16–24; and Robinson, review of Dam, *op. cit.*
15. The Continental Shelf Act (Section 9(3)) actually left a loophole for direct sales to industry by North Sea producers if the nationalised gas industry would not offer a 'reasonable price'. The producing companies were left in no doubt that there was no chance of their using the loophole. See Robinson, *Competition for Fuel*, *op. cit.*, p. 20.

16. The Corporation's purchase price for natural gas in 1975–76 (presumably including relatively expensive liquefied gas from Algeria) is shown in the 1977 Digest of Energy Statistics (Table 83) as 1.79p/therm. The average value per ton of imported crude oil in 1975 (Table 92 of the Digest) is £39.73 per ton – approximately 9.3p/therm at 426 therms per ton. The average value of imported crude rose to £52.5 per ton (12.3p/therm in 1976 but no information is given on the natural gas purchase price. Thus the natural gas price was about 19 per cent of the crude price in 1975/76 and probably lower in the following year.

17. Organisational slack is defined in R. M. Cyert and J. G. March, *A Behavioral Theory of the Firm*, (New Jersey: Prentice-Hall, 1963). See also Robinson, *Competition for Fuel, op. cit.*, pp. 21–2.

18. Between 1967 and 1969, 30 to 35 exploration wells per year were drilled in the southern North Sea. In the next seven years the annual average was 6 wells. See *Development of the Oil and Gas Resources of the United Kingdom, op. cit.*, Appendix 1.

19. See Dam, *op. cit.*, pp. 94–9.

20. See Geoffrey Heal, 'Economic Aspects of Natural Resource Depletion', in Pearce (ed.), *The Economics of Natural Resource Depletion, op. cit.*

21. See Robinson, *The Depletion of Energy Resources, op. cit.*; Robinson, *The Energy 'Crisis' and British Coal, op. cit.*; and Robinson, *Energy Depletion and the Economics of OPEC, op. cit.*

22. For some suggestions for the British fuel market see Robinson, *The Energy 'Crisis' and British Coal, op. cit.*

23. See Robinson and Morgan, 'Will North Sea Oil Save the British Economy!', *loc. cit.*, and 'The Economics of North Sea Oil Supplies', *loc. cit.*

24. Some further discussion of the market-versus-planning debate is in Robinson and Paul Remington, 'The Formulation of Energy Policy', *Petroleum Review*, London, September–October 1976.

25. Robinson and Morgan, *North Sea Oil and the British Economy, op. cit.*

26. Robinson and Morgan, *Effects of North Sea Oil on the United Kingdom Balance of Payments, op. cit.*

27. There may also be extra tax receipts (as compared with a situation of no North Sea oil) from relatively profitable activities supporting North Sea work (such as supplies of oil equipment and services).

28. In Chapter 5 it is shown that PRT payments are likely to be small *at 1977 prices*. The calculations shown in Table 9.3 assume higher prices, except for a few of the early years in the Limited Price Decline case. The estimates in Table 9.3 would be on the high side if sterling were to appreciate relative to the dollar so that oil prices and profits expressed in sterling were to fall. The sterling/dollar rate assumed in the table is $1.70 = £1.

29. Treasury estimates of receipts from royalty, PRT and Corporation Tax are £5000 million *at 1976 prices* over the five years 1976 to 1980, and about £3500 million a year *at 1976 prices* in the mid 1980s. See 'The North Sea and the UK Economy', *op. cit* Table 9.3 is in current prices.

30. See, for example, *Financial Times*, London, 20 September 1977 ('The North Sea Oil Factor').

31. This idea evidently has immense appeal to many journalists, with such honourable exceptions as Samuel Brittan ('Where to Invest North Sea Oil'),

Financial Times, London, 7 July 1977, and Patrick Hutber ('What – and What Not – to do with the Oil Money'), *Sunday Telegraph*, (London, 21 August 1977).

32. Brittan, *loc. cit.*
33. Harry G. Johnson, 'Planning and the Market in Economic Development', in *Money, Trade and Economic Growth* (London: Allen & Unwin, 1962) p. 154.

Index

211